JOHN LENNON & ME

A Play in Three Acts

by

CHERIE BENNETT

Based on the novel *Good-bye, Best Friend*

by

CHERIE BENNETT

Dramatic Publishing

Woodstock, Illinois • London, England • Melbourne, Australia

For all the people who know what it feels like
to be on the outside looking in.

JOHN LENNON & ME was publicly workshopped under the title *CANDY STORE WINDOW* at Mississippi State University, Starkville, Mississippi, October 22-26, 1992, under the direction of Dr. Jeffery Elwell.

Star	Molly Burns
Courtney Cambridge	Heidi Bevill
Sally Kasem	Sarah Ashmore
Dr. Scott Rhodes	Ryan Lamar
Nurse Janice Bobrin	Lucy Fullen
Ina "The Torturer" Tortunesky	Holly Hunter
Julie Rowen	Brittany Bill
Claudia Grubner	Christy Brumfield
Jeff Levine	Chris Reed
Tom Lowell	Andrew Watkins
Annie	Danielle Louys

JOHN LENNON & ME received its world premiere on March 29, 1993, at the Shalom Theatre, Jewish Community Center of Nashville, Nashville, Tennessee, under the direction of Cherie Bennett, associate director Robert Kiefer, produced by Shalom Theatre and Jeff Gottesfeld, Esq.

Star	Julia McFerrin
Courtney Cambridge	Jennie Smith
Sally Kasem	Lana Taradash
Dr. Scott Rhodes	Robert Locknar
Nurse Janice Bobrin	Marcy Murphree
Ina "The Torturer" Tortunesky	Layne Sasser
Julie Rowen	Jodi Kraft
Claudia Grubner	Tamara Tweedy
Jeff Levine	Ryan Shogrun
Tom Lowell	Andy Delicata
Flunkies	Yoni Limor, Ben Wolf
Additional teens	Sara Maceyunas, Michelle Haas, Irene Friedlander, Jack Frost, Sara Fuchs

The world professional premiere was at The Phoenix Theatre, Indianapolis, Indiana, in the summer of 1993.

JOHN LENNON & ME

A Play in Three Acts
For 3 male and 7 female players, expandable*

CHARACTERS

STAR (aka Stella Grubner) . . . . 13, has cystic fibrosis
COURTNEY CAMBRIDGE . . . . 13, has rheumatic fever
SALLY KASEM . . . . 13, has brittle diabetes
JULIE ROWEN (can double as ANNIE and FLUNKY) . . . 13
TOM LOWELL (can double as LEE and FLUNKY) 13
JEFF LEVINE . . . . 15, on the verge of a breakdown
CLAUDIA GRUBNER . . . . 30-45, Star's mother
"THE TORTURER" (Ina Tortunesky) . . . . . . mid-40s or older,
a medical technician
DR. SCOTT RHODES . . . . . late 20s, chief pediatric resident
NURSE JANICE BOBRIN 20-35
FLUNKY #1 & FLUNKY #2 . . . . teenagers,
Star's magical assistants
LEE & ANNIE . . . . teenage patients

* CASTING NOTE: With doubling, the cast can be as
small as ten or as large as sixteen or more (by adding more
teens as patients or Flunkies) depending on the wishes of the
producer.

TIME: The present.

PLACE: HEART HOUSE
A residence attached to a hospital for seriously or
terminally ill young people, in Nashville, Tennessee.

WHAT PEOPLE ARE SAYING about *John Lennon & Me...*

"Excellent. Both hilarious and deeply moving. Great for a high school production. We blew away the audience with this show. They didn't know what to expect, and they were quite pleased."
Scott Schwarz,
Baraga High School, Baraga, Mich.

"*John Lennon & Me* is a tremendously moving play. The characters were wonderfully written and a marvelous challenge to play." *Drama Dir., Chestermere High School,*
Calgary AB Canada

"My kids have been touched deeply by the characters in this play. It is fun to do and fun to watch. It is a perfect play for a middle school." *Chris Day,*
Grace Christian School, Raleigh, N.C.

"This is one of the most wonderful experiences my cast/crew and I have had! *J.L. & Me* was beautifully written, fun to rehearse, brought us all closer, and was loved by our audiences!"
Terri Woodd,
Riverview High School, Sarasota, Fla.

ACT ONE

AT RISE: *The stage is lit as the audience enters. The barest elements of the set are in place, fully seen by the audience. The last song on a half-hour pre-set tape (could be all old Beatles tunes) might be* "She Loves You." *The house lights remain on until STAR asks for them to be turned off during her opening monologue. As the song begins, all the FLUNKIES appear on stage. During the song they dress the entire set in perfectly synchronized movements. It should be comic, clever, a whirlwind. They finish exactly as the song finishes. STAR has, several minutes earlier, casually taken a seat in the house as if she were simply another member of the audience. She wears an oversized t-shirt with a picture of John Lennon on it, over which is a flashy denim jacket, jeans, and a backwards New York Jets baseball-style cap. She carries a small backpack and a portable tape deck. When the opening song ends and the FLUNKIES finish, she stands up in the aisle of the theatre and gets the audience's attention, addressing them conversationally. There is something of the stand-up comic about her.*

STAR. Excuse me, could I have everyone's attention? Hey, over here! *(She ad libs with some audience members, shaking hands, complimenting them on their outfits as she heads towards the stage.)* What's your name? *(Audience member gives name.)* Audience, I'd like you to meet *(That person's name.)* And *(That person's name.)* I'd like you to meet the audience! Let's all say hello to *(That person's name.)* On the count of three, hello *(That person's name.)* One, two, three—HELLO *(She says that person's name with the entire audience.).* Cool! You guys are great! So, listen, is everyone comfortable? *(She checks with someone in the front row.)* Good, because I know how it sucks if, like, your butt is stuck to the seat or you have to pee or something. Listen, before we go any further, I want to introduce you to the hardest working dudes in show business, my buds, my homies, the Flunkies! *(The FLUNKIES hit muscle poses.)* Let's give 'em a round of applause! Thanks! Bye guys, see ya later! *(FLUNKIES jog off.)* Hey, you in the booth! Kill the house lights! *(The house lights go out. A spot remains on STAR.)* Thanks! Allow me to introduce myself. Contrary to what it says on my birth certificate, my name is not Stella Grubner. I renamed myself Star—no last name, thank-you-very-much. I mean, Stella?? What could my parents have been thinking?? Well, Claudia, my mother—you'll meet her later—tells me that when I was born, she and my father lived in New York City. She was an actress and my dad was a stand-up comic. When my mom got pregnant with me, she was in rehearsal for a revival of this famous play, *A Streetcar Named Desire.* Because of me, she had to drop out. So she named me Stella, after the character she never got to play. My dad split when I was, like, two. Then Claudia ran out of money, which is how we ended up moving to Franklin, this little town outside of Nashville, into my grandparents' house. I plan to run away to New York when I'm seventeen, to become a very famous actress. I figure the sooner the better, since there's a chance I won't live to see my twentieth birthday. Not that I buy that. But the thing is, I have cystic fibrosis. I was born with it. Don't worry *(She says the name of the audience member we met earlier.)*, it's not catchy. When I was ten I looked it up in a medical dictionary. After all the technical stuff, it said: "the average life expectancy is twenty-five years. This disease is always fatal." Fatal. As in dead. I admit that one threw me for a minute. But then I read that last line again. "The average life expectancy is twenty-five years." Well, I am not average. I am extraordinary. So, right then I decided I'm not going to die. I'm just not.

(A light comes up on a girlie-looking room with twin beds, complete with icky precious inspirational posters.)

STAR. That's my room at Heart House. It's a place for sick kids. I've probably slept more nights there than I've slept in my own bed. The good news is it doesn't look like a hospital. The bad news is that if I'm at Heart House, it means my health has taken *(Melodramatically.)* A Turn For The Worse. *(The light goes out on the room.)* I got admitted again a few weeks ago—and I thought it would be the usual, no problem, you know? But it wasn't. Everything changed. If I live long enough to get really famous, I'll tell it on "Letterman." But just in case I don't, I'll tell you the whole thing now. And it's the total truth, or my name isn't Star.

(Blackout. A song, such as the one that was played at opening, blasts from STAR's portable tape deck. Lights up on a hallway. She turns down the music, and we hear kids' voices calling to her as she walks down the hall towards the room. She waves regally to them.)

LEE *(offstage)*. Star! Looking good!

STAR. Yo, Lee, how they hanging?

ANNIE *(offstage)*. Hey, Star! Welcome home!

STAR. Home?? Get a grip, Annie!

KEVIN *(offstage)*. Whoa, Star, great jacket! Where'd ya get it?

STAR. One of my lovers—Jim Carrey, I think. *(She enters the room and throws her backpack on the bed closest to the window and turns both inspirational posters around. On the back of one is an autographed poster of Patrick Swayze covered with kiss marks, the other is a poster of John Lennon covered with kiss marks. Sarcastically.)* Ah, Heart House, how do I love thee? Let me count the ways.

(STAR plops down on the bed. SALLY KASEM appears at the door.)

SALLY. Hi! *(Freezes in the doorway, a juvenile, too-eager grin on her face.)*

STAR *(to audience)*. That's Sally Kasem. She's a brittle diabetic. Plus, she's a few fries short of a "Happy Meal," if you catch my drift. *(Re-enters scene.)*

SALLY. Where have you been?

STAR. Home.

SALLY. Really? That's a coincidence! I was home, too!

STAR *(to audience)*. You see what I mean. *(Re-enters scene.)*

SALLY. I don't know how you do it, Star, but you always do it. I begged to get the corner room this time, but there was totally no way. I'm stuck in 1-A with some asthmatic kid who talks out loud to her Barbies.

STAR. Gruesome.

SALLY. And you waltz in and get the corner room again. Hey, maybe I could transfer in here!

STAR. Nope. I'm getting a roommate. Janice told me downstairs. Her name is Courtney something-or-other. She's never been here before.

SALLY. Well, I don't see why some new girl should get the best room. Do you think that's fair? Because I don't.

STAR. How come you're here again, anyway?

SALLY. Oh, they need to regulate my insulin again or something. I don't see why I have to have insulin.

STAR. Because you have diabetes.

SALLY. Well, yeah, I know that. But it isn't fair! How come you're back?

STAR. Same old same old. So, how's the local talent?

SALLY *(stymied for a moment, then she gets it)*. Oh! You mean *(She spells.)* B-O-Y-S! A bunch of babies. Oh, except for one cute guy in 2-B. He just came in yesterday. I saw him go into his room, but I didn't talk to him. Other than that, there's just Dr. Scott.

STAR. Never say "just" before you say "Dr. Scott."

(As if on cue, DR. SCOTT RHODES appears in the doorway and freezes in some macho pose, revealing a Superman t-shirt under his lab coat.)

STAR *(addressing audience)*. Tell me he isn't a total hunk. Claudia says he has "body of death." Fortunately, Claudia is too old for him, whereas I am mature for my age. *(Reenters scene.)* Yo! Dr. Scott!

DR. SCOTT *(closes lab coat, bounds into the room, gives SALLY a small wave and crosses to hug STAR)*. Hey, kiddo! Janice told me you were here. I thought I'd pop in and say hello.

STAR. Hi!

DR. SCOTT. How ya doing?

STAR. Oh, fine.

DR. SCOTT *(doubting)*. Star...

STAR *(reluctantly)*. Okay, I coughed up some blood last night. Not much, though.

DR. SCOTT. Dr. Pemrose said to start you on IV antibiotics.

STAR. Yeah. I feel great, though. Don't I look great?

SALLY. You're not supposed to fish for compliments. Right, Dr. Scott?

STAR *(ignoring SALLY)*. Well, don't I?

DR. SCOTT *(laughing)*. Yeah, you look great. Your hair got longer.

STAR. That's because I haven't been here for three months— I think that's a record for me. Not that I didn't pine away for you and everything. *(SALLY giggles. STAR shoots her a look that says "You are so juvenile.")*

DR. SCOTT. You are going to be hazardous to some guy's health when you start dating.

STAR. Not some guy, lots of guys...I hope! Hey, you want to come back later and play some poker? I brought my lucky deck!

DR. SCOTT. Last time we played for pennies you took five bucks off me. I think your lucky deck is only lucky for you.

STAR. Well, of course. That's the whole poi—*(She begins to cough, a dry, metallic sound. She has trouble catching her breath. DR. SCOTT soothes her until she stops coughing.)*

DR. SCOTT. Better? *(STAR nods.)* How many thumps are you doing each day?

STAR *(still trying to catch her breath)*. Please. Don't talk to me about thumps. At home Claudia's giving me two, but The Torturer says I have to start doing three a day. It's her idea of a good time.

(A light comes up on the opposite side of the stage. We hear THE TORTURER'S theme music: maybe "Jaws." We see INA TORTUNESKY, aka THE TORTURER. She wears a nurse's uniform and army boots.)

STAR *(to audience)*. That's her, Mrs. Tortunesky—The Torturer. If she was green she could pass for The Incredible Hulk. She used to be an army nurse, but she retired. Personally, I think she did this just so she could make my life miserable. Whenever I'm at Heart House, she wakes me up every morning at six a.m. for physical therapy by barking commands in my face. *(As THE TORTURER barks her commands straight out to the audience, STAR lip-synchs the words at the same time.)*

THE TORTURER *(whacking the air with her hand)*. Lie still! Turn over! Now, cough! Cough!

STAR *(to audience)*. All the time she's yelling this stuff, she's whacking me as hard as she can. It's supposed to keep me from choking to death on—okay, this is disgusting—thick mucus. Personally, I'd like to whack her to death! After that I have to breathe this crap called Pulmozyme through an oxygen mask, and then she whacks the hell out of me again. I really hate her. *(The light goes out on THE TORTURER. STAR re-enters scene.)*

DR. SCOTT. She's actually not a bad person. She's just kind of...serious.

STAR. Serious? She's sadistic! I heard she whacked one CF kid so hard he flew off the bed and landed in the corner like a hockey puck. And then she yelled *(Star imitates THE TORTURER.)* "Score!!"

SALLY *(giggling)*. Wow, that's great, you sound just like her!

DR. SCOTT. I admit you have talent, but you have to realize, she's trying to help you.

STAR. Go back to the part about how I have talent.

DR. SCOTT. Maybe you'll become an actress.

STAR. Maybe? Do you realize there are thirteen-year-olds starring in TV series, and in really big movies? I'm getting too old to be discovered young!

SALLY *(to DR. SCOTT)*. Everything is so dramatic with her.

STAR *(with dignity)*. That's because I'm a professional thespian.

(From the hallway we hear a female voice singing something like "Oklahoma!" with great enthusiasm. NURSE JANICE BOBRIN, the owner of the voice, appears in the doorway and freezes, a manic grin on her face.)

STAR *(to audience)*. That's Janice Bobrin, one of the live-in nurses. She gives new meaning to the word "perky."

JANICE *(rushing to STAR)*. How's my favorite singing partner?

STAR *(back in the scene)*. Still tone-deaf.

JANICE. Oh, pooh, that doesn't matter! Hey, tonight is sing-along night in the lounge! Isn't that great? I got the sheet music for "Oklahoma!" *(Or another appropriate song.)*

STAR *(to audience)*. Who would have guessed. *(Re-enters scene.)*

JANICE. I taught Sally yesterday so that she could help lead the sing-along! She's my super helper, aren't you?

SALLY. I guess so.

JANICE *(clearly in love with DR. SCOTT)*. You'll be there, won't you, Dr. Scott?

DR. SCOTT *(trying to figure out how to get out of it)*. Gee, I—

JANICE. It'll be so much fun! It starts out: *(She starts to sing.)* Come on, Sally, you join in! *(JANICE and SALLY sing badly together.)*

STAR *(over their singing).* Isn't there, like, a mime section you could teach?

DR. SCOTT *(over their singing).* Gee, would you look at the time—

(Into the doorway steps COURTNEY CAMBRIDGE. She holds a small suitcase, a stuffed animal, and looks scared to death. She is dressed in expensive frills, a hair bow, and patent leather shoes, as if she was 8 instead of 13. Everyone notices her and all the noise stops.)

COURTNEY *(clearing her throat).* I...I...

STAR *(to audience).* My roommate, Courtney Cambridge. Prettier than me. Taller than me. Tits. It was hate at first sight. *(Re-enters scene.)*

COURTNEY. I'm sorry to interrupt...

DR. SCOTT. Courtney!

COURTNEY. Am I in the right room?

DR. SCOTT. Sure you are! Everybody, this is Courtney Cambridge, one of my favorite patients.

COURTNEY *(faltering at the door).* Maybe I should have waited downstairs with my parents...

DR. SCOTT *(leading COURTNEY into the room).* No, no, it's fine. *(DR. SCOTT puts his arm around COURTNEY's shoulder.)*

STAR *(to audience).* One of his favorite patients? And he had his arm around her! His hand was extremely close to her left boob. He didn't have his arm around me and I didn't have a left boob *or* a right boob. I felt like snatching her perfect blonde hair out of her head. Dr. Scott introduced her to everybody, saving me for last. *(Re-enters scene.)*

DR. SCOTT. And this is your roommate, Star.

COURTNEY *(wide-eyed)*. Your name is really Star?

STAR *(too, too bored)*. Uh-huh. *(DR. SCOTT leads COURTNEY to the other twin bed, where she sits on the very edge. SALLY reluctantly rises.)*

DR. SCOTT. Are your parents downstairs?

COURTNEY *(nodding)*. Filling out forms.

STAR. That'll take forever.

DR. SCOTT *(gently, to COURTNEY)*. Why don't you lie down?

COURTNEY *(clutching her stuffed animal for dear life)*. No, no, I'm fine.

JANICE. I hope you'll come to our sing-a-long tonight, Courtney! Sally, right now you and I have a date to take some of your blood.

SALLY *(moving reluctantly towards the door)*. It isn't fair! I feel like a pincushion!

JANICE. Oh, pooh. Come on, we'll sing. It'll help, you'll see! *(JANICE puts her arm around SALLY and leads her out, singing again.)*

DR. SCOTT. You just relax, Courtney. You'll have another EKG soon, and I'll be back to see you later.

COURTNEY. Okay.

STAR *(calling to DR. SCOTT)*. Hey, don't forget our poker date! You bring the beer!

DR. SCOTT. Be nice. *(DR. SCOTT exits.)*

COURTNEY. They let you have beer?

STAR. Sure. And on Sundays we have champagne.

COURTNEY. That's a joke. Right?

STAR *(to audience)*. And I thought Sally was dumb. *(Re-enters scene.)*

COURTNEY *(looking at the poster of John Lennon).* I really like your poster.

STAR. He was the most talented person who ever lived. And he died so young.

COURTNEY *(horrified).* Paul McCartney is dead???

STAR. That's Lennon. John Lennon.

COURTNEY. Oh. Sorry.

STAR *(to audience).* She's killing me. *(Re-enters scene.)* So. How old are you?

COURTNEY. Thirteen.

STAR. Same as me. What are you in for? *(STAR starts coughing deeply. She's embarrassed, and finally gets control of it.)*

COURTNEY. Do you have a bad cold or something?

STAR. Cystic fibrosis. It's this lung thing—no problem. So what about you?

COURTNEY *(in a shaky voice).* I'm not sure. I just had this bad sore throat. I didn't tell my mom right away because I didn't want to miss the big away game we had. So then it got worse and worse. It turned out to be strep throat, and that turned into rheumatic fever. And now they think it did something to my heart.

STAR. Can't be that bad. Your lips and your nails aren't blue. If something is mega-wrong with your heart, you turn blue.

COURTNEY. Are you sure?

STAR. Yep.

COURTNEY. Thanks for telling me. No one will tell me anything.

STAR. Yeah, well, that's how doctors are.

COURTNEY. I've never been sick before. Well, I had the measles when I was a kid, but you know what I mean.

STAR *(breezily).* Oh, sure.

COURTNEY. You don't seem very sick, either. Except for your cough.

STAR. No problem.

COURTNEY. Yeah, I guess not. (*COURTNEY relaxes a little. She settles back on the bed. Confidentially.*) You know, I was so nervous coming up here. Walking down the hall, I saw some really sick-looking kids. Two of them were bald!

STAR. Chemo.

COURTNEY. That means they have cancer, right? It was so horrible! I just prayed I wouldn't have a really sick roommate.

STAR. Why?

COURTNEY. It would be so embarrassing, like when my best friend comes to visit me, you know?

STAR. Oh, sure. My friends come visit me all the time, too. So I'm glad to have a normal roommate, myself. (*To audience*). Yeah, like I was really going to tell her that I actually didn't have any friends outside of Heart House. It's hard to make friends when you don't go to school. So sue me. I lied. (*Re-enters scene.*)

COURTNEY. I'm so glad you're normal!

SHRILL WOMAN'S VOICE (*from hall*). Yoo-hoo, Courtney! Where's my baby?

COURTNEY. Oh, God, it's my mother.

STAR (*to audience*). I'll do you a big favor and skip over the part where her parental units showed up. Her mother was so suffocating, she actually sucked all the air out of the room. (*Re-enters scene.*)

SHRILL WOMAN'S VOICE (*from hall*). Bye, baby! I'll be back first thing in the morning. Do everything the doctor says!

COURTNEY (*waves bye-bye, then turns to STAR*). I hate my mother.

STAR. Well, of course.

COURTNEY. If it was up to her, I'd stay a child forever. She'd have me in frills and patent leather party shoes if she could get away with it. (*COURTNEY looks down at herself. Clearly her mother has gotten away with it.*)

STAR. Gross.

COURTNEY. She's worse than any of my friends' mothers. They always tease me about how naive I am. And it's all because my stupid mom barely lets me out of the house without a chaperone! Is your mom like that, too?

STAR. Not exactly. You'd have to meet Claudia to know what I mean.

COURTNEY. You call your mother Claudia?

STAR. It's her name.

COURTNEY. Wow. I can't believe I have to be here. It's all my mother's fault. I'm missing cheerleading practice and everything!

STAR. You're a cheerleader?

COURTNEY. Head JV cheerleader at Donelson Christian Academy. Where do you go?

STAR. I've been educated privately.

COURTNEY. What does that mean?

STAR. You know. Tutors. At home. All us professional actresses do it that way.

COURTNEY. You are not. All they make in Nashville is country music videos. All the movies are made in Hollywood. And you don't live in Hollywood.

STAR. That is why God created airplanes.

COURTNEY (*skeptical*). What movie were you ever in?

STAR. Did you see *Hot House Princess*?

COURTNEY. Are you kidding? I saw it four times with my best friend.

STAR. I'm in it. *(She addresses audience.)* For once I was actually telling the truth. They filmed the outdoor dance sequences in Memphis. Naturally Claudia got hired right away. Then I got picked to play a teenybopper dancing to this old Beatles song, "She Loves You," in a scene with about a hundred other teenyboppers. I ended up in Heart House afterwards with a bad pneumonia, but it was worth it. So I told her the whole story. I might have exaggerated just a little. *(Re-enters scene.)*

COURTNEY. You actually had lunch with Patrick Swayze??

STAR. Yep. *(To audience.)* Actually, I had lunch in the same room with Patrick Swayze, as did about three hundred other extras. *(Re-enters scene.)*

COURTNEY. That is so awesome.

(JANICE enters wheeling an EKG machine. She wheels it over to COURTNEY's bed.)

JANICE. Hey, y'all! Everything peachy?

STAR. Peachy.

JANICE. Time for your EKG, Courtney.

COURTNEY. I'd rather not.

JANICE. We just need some info on that little ol' ticker. It won't take but a minute.

COURTNEY. I know. I still hate it.

JANICE *(closing the curtains around COURTNEY's bed).* Oh, pooh.

COURTNEY *(from behind the curtain).* Star? Could you talk to me?

JANICE *(from behind the curtain).* Hold still while I attach these cute little electrodes to your chest. It'll be okay, sweetie.

COURTNEY. Star?

STAR *(calling in to COURTNEY)*. Actually, she's telling the truth. An EKG is one of the few things they can do to you here that really doesn't hurt. *(To audience)*. While Courtney lay there, I explained their codes. For example, if they say: "it won't hurt a bit," that means "of course it's going to hurt, but I'm trying to get you to be cooperative." If they say "All you'll feel is some discomfort," it means they're going to kill you. I talked to Courtney through the entire EKG. As you know, monologues are my long suit. *(Re-enters scene.)*

JANICE *(pulling back the curtain)*. All done! That wasn't so bad, was it? I'll see y'all later!

(JANICE wheels the EKG to the door and exits just as JULIE ROWEN appears in the doorway. She wears a cheerleader's uniform. If possible, JULIE should do gymnastics or twirl a baton during this scene.)

JULIE. Courtney?

COURTNEY. Julie! *(JULIE and COURTNEY scream simultaneously.)*

JULIE *(runs to COURTNEY and hugs her)*. Omigosh, did I, like, hurt you?

COURTNEY. I'm not breakable, you idiot. I'm so glad you're here! Can you believe I'm in this prison?

JULIE *(pulling up a chair by the bed)*. Bogus. You look, like, normal! I mean, really, like normal. Like, totally normal!

COURTNEY. I am normal!

STAR. Yeah, it's this place that isn't.

COURTNEY. Oh, this is my roommate, Star. And this is my best friend, Julie.

JULIE *(ignoring STAR)*. This place is, like, seriously creepy. I went down the wrong corridor, and there's this room with a big red sign on the door that says "Caution! Isolation!" And I looked inside, and there's this real skinny kid in there, like, coughing up blood! It has to be AIDS!

COURTNEY. I'm staying someplace where there's AIDS??

JULIE. I walked as far away from the kid's door as I could. Do you think I need to, like, wash my hands?

STAR (*to audience*). I knew the kid they were talking about. Lee Fury. He's got tutors, too, just like me. Actually I went to regular school for a while, in fourth grade. But I coughed up blood and all the kids ran out of the room, screaming "AIDS! AIDS!" It was the most embarrassing moment of my life. (*Re-enters scene.*)

JULIE. Listen, I can only stay a minute. I had to, like, sneak out of cheerleading practice behind Lundgren's back and run all the way over here.

COURTNEY. Wow, Lundgren will kill you.

JULIE. I know! If she could ever catch me! But she can't!

COURTNEY. Listen, who knows I'm here?

JULIE. No one! I mean, just me.

COURTNEY. Besides you. Does Tom know? Because I will die if Tom knows.

JULIE. He doesn't, I swear! Everyone at school is, like, talking, because you've been out so long. I just said you had a bad flu.

COURTNEY. You won't tell?

JULIE. Of course I won't tell, you idiot. I would never, ever, ever tell on you! My mom knows, though, because your mom told her, and you know my mom has—

JULIE & COURTNEY (*simultaneously*). —The biggest mouth on the planet.

COURTNEY. I'm totally ruined.

JULIE. I told her not to tell. I'll tell her again.

COURTNEY. Make her promise.

JULIE. I will. God, I gotta boogie. If Lundgren realizes I'm gone she'll probably, like, give birth. Good thing I'm a fast runner! *(She hugs COURTNEY.)* I love you to death!

STAR. We try not to say that word here. *(JULIE laughs, sprints to the door and exits.)* Nice girl, very chatty, slightly hyper.

COURTNEY. Julie is my best friend in the entire world.

STAR. I guess you have tons of friends.

COURTNEY. Well, sure.

STAR. Oh, me, too.

COURTNEY. So, do you have a boyfriend?

STAR. I have tons of those, too.

COURTNEY. You've got tons of boyfriends?

STAR. Actors.

COURTNEY. I only have one. At least, I think he's my boyfriend. His name is Tom Lowell. He invited me to our school's dance next month. Does that make him my boyfriend?

STAR. Maybe. But maybe he only did it because his mother made him. Or to make someone jealous.

COURTNEY. He wouldn't do that. Would he?

STAR *(on a roll, making it up as she goes along)*. Depends. I once played the part of this girl who only pretends to like this guy because she's really in love with...his older brother. She even Does It with the younger brother, just to prove to the older brother that she doesn't care! Then, the older brother falls madly, passionately in love with her, but by that time she's already Done It with the younger guy, so she's so bummed out that she tries to kill herself—

COURTNEY. Omigosh, that's so terrible!

STAR *(smug)*. Well, that was just made up by some brilliant artist. I'm sure Tom really likes you.

COURTNEY. What was it, a movie?

STAR. No.

COURTNEY. A play?

STAR. A...scene from a play.

COURTNEY. So who wrote it?

STAR. I...sort of did.

COURTNEY. So where was it performed?

STAR *(to audience)*. If she laughed at me she was dead meat. *(Re- enters scene.)* Here...sort of.

COURTNEY. Wow, that is so cool. You act and write. You're really talented.

STAR. True.

COURTNEY. Where do you get your ideas?

STAR. Life.

COURTNEY. You mean you actually fell in love with the older brother of one of your boyfriends?

STAR. Yes. And the really awful thing is...he's right here in Heart House this very minute!

COURTNEY. No!

STAR. Yes! He's in...2-B!! *(To audience.)* Okay, right now you're saying to yourself: "This girl is a total liar." All I really knew about the guy in 2-B was what Sally had told me, and that wasn't much. Sometimes I get carried away with my own creative genius. *(Re-enters scene.)*

COURTNEY. What are you going to do?

(We hear THE TORTURER'S theme music once again. It grows louder as THE TORTURER enters.)

THE TORTURER. Good afternoon.

STAR *(from under the pillow)*. What's so good about it?

THE TORTURER *(crosses to STAR and pulls the pillow off her head)*. So, I haven't seen you in three months. We have much work to do. *(As she speaks, she arranges the pillows on Star's bed for her therapy. COURTNEY stares at THE TORTURER in frightened fascination.)*

STAR. Where are your manners? You could at least say hello to Courtney, my new roommate.

THE TORTURER *(stepping menacingly towards COURTNEY)*. You don't have cystic fibrosis, correct?

COURTNEY *(staring in horror)*. No! No, I swear I don't!

THE TORTURER. No need to stare, young lady. *(THE TORTURER sets up the oxygen mask with the Pulmozyme. Then she pulls the curtain shut which divides the beds, but the curtain stops before the view of STAR's bed is closed from our view.)*

STAR. The runner's broken on my side. *(COURTNEY has turned around in bed so that she can see beyond the edge of the curtain. She watches in morbid fascination. STAR has turned around in bed, and can see COURTNEY's face beyond the curtain. To THE TORTURER.)* Got any dirty pictures of your husband?

THE TORTURER. Of course not!

STAR. Wanna buy some? *(THE TORTURER sees the girls looking at each other, and tries to close the curtain, but fails.)* Might as well give up. Courtney is going to witness your crime.

THE TORTURER. Enough levity. We have work to do.

STAR *(to COURTNEY)*. Watch closely. You are about to see a thirteen-year-old girl whacked to death.

THE TORTURER. Nonsense, all you'll experience is…*(She laughs ominously.)* "some discomfort." *(THE TORTURER stands over STAR and raises her arm for the first blow. She freezes.)*

STAR. Hold that thought.

(STAR moves out from under THE TORTURER's hand, a FLUNKY throws a life-sized stuffed dummy of STAR through the window, onto the bed. STAR walks downstage. Another FLUNKY hands STAR a microphone. STAR looks back at THE TORTURER.)

STAR. Much better. *(A FLUNKY rings a bell, and we hear pre-recorded noise of a huge crowd at a prize fight. THE TORTURER gives the dummy exaggerated therapy, whacking it viciously on the chest and back, then beating the dummy to a pulp, à la the World Wrestling Federation, as STAR watches and narrates the action to the audience in the style of a prize-fight announcer. Into the mike.)* And it's THE TORTURER, moving in fast, striking the first blows. A left jab! Another! She hooks to the body! Ouch! A huge right cross! Oh, ladies and gentlemen, our champ is taking a tremendous pounding! *(THE TORTURER slaps an oxygen mask of Pulmozyme on the dummy's face.)* What's this? The champ needs oxygen! Is she going down, folks?? *(THE TORTURER moves the oxygen mask and whacks harder.)* But, no! Our champ is still in the game! What grit! What fortitude! What a true champion! *(The crowd cheering noises crescendo, STAR holds her hands together over her head in victory, then she runs back into the scene, throws the dummy out the window into the arms of a FLUNKY, then smoothly slides into bed, a boxing ring bell sounding as THE TORTURER finishes.)*

THE TORTURER. You were very congested. We'll have to work harder this evening. *(THE TORTURER exits.)*

COURTNEY. Star? Are you okay?

(At the door is CLAUDIA GRUBNER, Star's mother. She wears a motorcycle jacket [or a denim jacket identical to Star's], t-shirt and jeans.)

CLAUDIA *(entering the room).* Sure, she's okay. My girl's always okay, right?

STAR *(exhausted, struggling to sit up).* Sure. No problem.

CLAUDIA *(kisses STAR and sits).* I am pooped, girlfriend. I had the most rotten day. *(CLAUDIA notices COURTNEY and gives her a friendly wave.)* Hi, I'm Star's mom. Call me Claudia.

COURTNEY. Claudia. Okay, Claudia. My name is Courtney, Claudia.

STAR *(to audience).* Clearly Courtney wasn't used to calling someone's mother by her first name. But as you can see, my mother doesn't look like anyone's mother. I really like Claudia, and Claudia really likes me, but she doesn't like my disease. I think it scares her too much, which scares me too much, so we never talk about it. I act like it's no big thing, and she acts like she believes me. This is just the way it is. *((Re-enters scene.)*

CLAUDIA. I taught a beginners' ballet class that started this morning. It was a new low in the art form. This overweight woman who danced maybe a hundred years ago in some community theatre thing insists she should go on toe. On toe! No toe could take that kind of punishment! *(CLAUDIA rummages in her purse looking for hard candy.)* So, what's kickin', chickens?

STAR. The usual. No biggie.

CLAUDIA. You're such a trouper. *(CLAUDIA finds the candy and pops one in her mouth. She throws one to each of the girls. To COURTNEY).* This is supposed to make me not want cigarettes.

COURTNEY. Is it working?

CLAUDIA. No. I still crave cigarettes, only now I've gained five pounds from the stupid candy!

COURTNEY. You teach dance, right?

CLAUDIA. You got it.

COURTNEY. I always wanted to take ballet, but my mother said my ankles were too weak. And I don't have weak ankles! She's just afraid of everything!

CLAUDIA. That's a drag. Maybe we can work something out when you get out of here.

COURTNEY. Really? That would be terrific! Hey, I heard about you being in *Hot House Princess* and everything.

CLAUDIA. I even danced in that big outdoor dance scene with Patrick Swayze.

COURTNEY. No!

CLAUDIA. Yeah! He dipped me!

COURTNEY. I remember that! Hey, I think I recognize you!

CLAUDIA. Cool.

COURTNEY. Wait 'til I tell Julie. She's my best friend. Hey, I bet she'll want your autograph!

CLAUDIA. Sure, for whatever it's worth. So listen, I've got to go down and fill out some of those endless papers—I came up here first to tell you the big news. And I do mean big. Guess who's expecting a phone call from New York tonight?

STAR *(very excited)*. You got a part?

CLAUDIA. I don't want to jinx it by talking about it.

STAR. It's a part! I know it's a part! Off-Broadway? On Broadway??

CLAUDIA. Let's just say I better keep these dancing legs in primo shape. Later! *(CLAUDIA exits.)*

COURTNEY. Your mother is unbelievably fabulous.

STAR. I know.

COURTNEY. Why couldn't my father have married someone like her?

STAR. Because then there'd be no you.

COURTNEY *(thinking a moment)*. You know, I thought that being here would be the worst thing in the entire world. But...it's not so bad. I guess maybe they put us together because we're not as sick as the others.

STAR. Probably.

COURTNEY *(gets up and crosses to the bathroom, turns around. Shyly)*. I'm really glad you're my roommate.

STAR. It's gonna be a riot. *(COURTNEY exits into the bathroom. To audience.)* So we were going to be friends. Imagine that. Maybe we'd even stay friends after Courtney got out and went home. I'd had roommates that had said we'd stay friends, but as soon as they got sprung, they forgot all about me. Not that I blamed them. Who wanted to be reminded of a place where all the kids were sick, where some kids actually died? But maybe Courtney was different. And all I had to do was to spend twenty-four hours a day pretending I wasn't really very sick at all. No problem.

(Crossfade to a comfortable lounge, full of icky, cheery, inspirational posters. SALLY sits with NURSE JANICE as she plays the guitar and sings something like "Puff the Magic Dragon." LEE and ANNIE attempt to trim DR. SCOTT's hair, ignoring the bad singing as much as possible.)

JANICE. Hey, y'all! Come on and sing with us! You'll love it!

ANNIE. Sha, right.

JANICE. But it's "Puff"! *(Or another appropriate song)* Everybody loves "Puff"!

ANNIE. Survey says… *(ANNIE, LEE and SALLY cross their arms to make a huge "X," and then make the "wrong answer" buzzer noise à la "Family Feud.")*

JANICE. Oh, pooh, come on! It's fun!

LEE. No offense, Janice, but you're the worst guitar player in Nashville.

JANICE. It's the spirit that counts, right, Dr. Scott? *(The kids make kissing noises. They all know JANICE has a crush on DR. SCOTT.)*

DR. SCOTT. Right!

JANICE. Dr. Scott is going to join in on the next tune! It's one y'all love! "Kum Ba Yah"!

(JANICE starts playing and singing "Kum Ba Yah." KEVIN, LEE and ANNIE each put their finger down their throat and make gagging noises. STAR and COURTNEY appear at the door.)

STAR *(to COURTNEY)*. Oh no! She started early! It's "Kum Ba Yah" time.

COURTNEY. What's that?

STAR. That song she's singing.

JANICE. Come on, Dr. Scott! Join in!

DR. SCOTT. Pick a key! *(DR. SCOTT reluctantly joins JANICE and SALLY in singing "Kum Ba Yah.")*

STAR. I've asked everyone the same question. What does "Kum Ba Yah" mean? No one knows.

COURTNEY. It's stupid to sing a song when you don't know what you're singing about.

STAR. That's why I've decided it means "stinky farts." *(JANICE starts another verse, singing lustily. At the doorway, STAR and COURTNEY fall over each other laughing. JANICE encourages the other kids to join in, they reluc-*

*tantly do. The more people sing, the more STAR and
COURTNEY crack up. STAR makes fart noises on her arm.
SALLY stands up and weaves around the room. STAR is
trying to catch her breath from laughing.)* Look! Even
Sally can't take it!

COURTNEY. She looks like somebody spiked her milk!
*(SALLY stumbles, falls to the ground, her eyes roll back,
her arms and legs jerk uncontrollably. Everything stops.
NURSE JANICE goes to SALLY. DR. SCOTT jumps up and
gets a hypodermic needle and some medicine from his bag.
He quickly fills the syringe and injects SALLY.)*

DR. SCOTT. She'll be fine in a minute. She's in insulin
shock. *(COURTNEY stands there in shock. Then she goes
to SALLY and strokes her hair. The other kids look at
SALLY, then move away, expressionless. STAR looks at JA-
NICE and DR. SCOTT as they tend to SALLY, then she
walks downstage.)*

STAR *(to audience).* Here's the thing. When you're sick, I
mean really sick, like the you-don't-know-if-you'll-ever-
get-well kind of sick, or even scarier, the you-*know*-you'll-
never-get-well kind of sick, you live in a different world
from healthy kids. It's like...like walking by a candy store,
and you see all these kids inside, laughing, hanging out,
having a great time, but no matter what, you can never do
more than press your face against the glass. *(We hear the
song JANICE was singing, now plaintively being played on
a flute. STAR watches SALLY, as JANICE croons to her
softly, and the lights fade.)*

END OF ACT ONE

ACT TWO

AT RISE: *Two weeks later. Lights up on the lounge. SALLY sits by herself reading a paperback teen novel. KEVIN and LEE sit across the room playing with a Gameboy. STAR appears at the door. She is hooked up to an IV that she wheels around with her. The IV is decorated with a big smiley-face.*

STAR (*from the doorway*). Pssssst! Sally! (*SALLY ignores her, keeps reading.*) Sally! (*SALLY keeps reading. STAR crosses to SALLY and turns. She makes sure the kids across the room aren't listening.*) So, what did you find out?

SALLY. I'm not speaking to you.

STAR. Sure, you are.

SALLY. Okay, I just did. But now I'm not, right after I say that I have nothing to say to you. Why should I? It isn't fair. You never hang out with me anymore. You're too busy with your stuck-up roommate.

STAR. She's not stuck-up.

SALLY. She is, too. The only reason you're talking to me now is because you want to know what I found out about that guy in 2-B. Well, I don't have to tell you anything. You're not my best friend anymore.

STAR (*to audience*). Best friend? Sally thought I was her best friend? Now, that is really pathetic. But I couldn't let on, because at the moment she had something that I wanted. A

few days earlier I had bribed Sally with some Twinkies—
she wasn't supposed to have sweets and she craved them—
and I sent her on a mission: find out everything about the
guy in 2-B. After two weeks of making stuff up to
Courtney about my boyfriend, she naturally wanted to meet
him. Usually I would tell her I was going to his room, and
then I'd walk around the building a few times. Clearly, I
needed help fast. *(Re-enters scene.)* So did you find out
anything or not?

SALLY. Maybe I did and maybe I didn't. *(STAR sighs and
pulls a Twinkie out of her pocket, unwraps it, sniffs it and
ostentatiously goes for the first bite. SALLY grabs for it
and begins stuffing her face.)* He never comes down for
meals, so no one knows that much about him.

STAR. I already know that! *(STAR goes to grab back the
Twinkie. SALLY feints away with it.)*

SALLY *(stuffing her mouth).* His name is Jeff Levine. He's
fifteen.

STAR. Now we're getting somewhere!

SALLY. He's from Nashville. His parents are both professors
at Vanderbilt. He's five-eight, and has brown hair and blue
eyes. He goes to the University School, and he's captain of
the varsity tennis team.

STAR. Get down, Sally! How did you find all that out?

SALLY. Janice. I pumped her while I pretended to learn some
guitar chords.

STAR. You're a really good friend.

SALLY. You used to be a really good friend, too.

STAR. So why doesn't this Jeff guy ever come out of his
room?

SALLY *(shrugging).* Janice says he's sad.

STAR. Huh. *(Getting up.)* Thanks, Sally, I owe you one.

SALLY. Have fun with your snotty roommate.

(SALLY goes back to her book. STAR exits as the lights crossfade on the lounge, up on the bedroom. COURTNEY sits on her bed with JULIE. STAR enters.)

COURTNEY. This can't be happening! My life is ruined!

JULIE. I'm really sorry. But you know my mother. She can't keep her mouth shut!

STAR. What happened?

COURTNEY. Just the worst thing in the world. Julie's mom told Tom's mom I was in here. Tom's mom told Tom, and then Tom told Julie he's coming to visit me tonight after dinner!

STAR. So what's the biggie? That means he really likes you.

COURTNEY. Don't you understand? I don't want him to visit me here! It's not like I'm getting my tonsils out or something!

JULIE. But you're not like the other kids here. You're, like, normal!

COURTNEY. Everyone knows normal kids don't come to this place.

JULIE. I'm really sorry. I'd kill my mom for you if I thought I could, like, get away with it.

COURTNEY. At least you warned me. *(A car horn.)*

JULIE. I gotta motor, my mom wanted to come in with me but I, like, begged her to wait in the car.

COURTNEY. Well, thanks for that, anyway.

JULIE. I'll come back tomorrow. Can Beth and Amy and Shannon come?

COURTNEY. Sure, the whole cheerleading squad can come. Now that Tom knows, the entire school is going to find out anyway.

JULIE. Bye! I love you to de—oops! *(A car horn, more insistent.)* Okay, okay, keep your shirt on! *(JULIE continues babbling as she runs to the door and exits.)*

COURTNEY. He's never going to want to take me to the dance after he sees me in this place.

STAR. Sure he will.

COURTNEY. You don't understand. I don't know how to talk to him, even in school! It's horrible! Everyone thinks that just because I'm a cheerleader I must be really cool around boys, but I'm not.

STAR. What's the biggie? They're just people.

COURTNEY. No they're not. They're boys!

(DR. SCOTT enters the room.)

DR. SCOTT. How are my two favorite girls today?

STAR *(cheerfully)*. I'm fine. Courtney's life is ruined.

DR. SCOTT. What's wrong?

STAR. Her boyfriend is coming to visit her tonight.

DR. SCOTT. Hey, great! Courtney, we're going to start you on some intravenous antibiotics today. Same stuff you've been taking, but this should help you get better faster.

COURTNEY. Wait a second. Are you telling me that you're going to stick one of those *things* in my arm like Star has?

DR. SCOTT. It looks much worse than it actually feels.

COURTNEY. But...but you can't. Tom is coming!

DR. SCOTT. Sorry. Hey, I'm sure Tom wants you to get better. He'll understand. Janice will be in to hook you up in a little bit. It'll be fine, kiddo. *(DR. SCOTT pats COURTNEY's hand and exits.)*

COURTNEY. This is the worst day of my entire life. Tom is coming here and I won't be able to say a single word to him.

STAR. Sure you will!

COURTNEY. I won't! You don't understand because your boyfriend is in here with you. Why won't you tell me what's wrong with him?

STAR. It's kind of complicated, you see—

COURTNEY. I can't believe Tom is coming here. This is absolutely the worst day of my life.

STAR. It can't be that bad.

COURTNEY. It is! I know it wouldn't be for you, you can talk to anybody. You're an actress. But I can't! I just can't!

STAR *(getting an idea).* I'm brilliant!

COURTNEY. I know, but I'm not.

STAR. I mean I just got this incredible idea! I'll write a scene based on you and Tom. Then you'll be completely prepared when he shows up!

COURTNEY. You can do that?

STAR. Of course!

COURTNEY. But what about the IV?

STAR. We'll work that in. It's all in the presentation. Attitude is everything.

(JANICE appears at the door with an IV.)

JANICE. Time for your IV, sweetie! *(COURTNEY reluctantly holds out her arm. JANICE hooks her up to the IV.)*

STAR *(to audience).* While Courtney was getting stuck, I made a few mental notes. She needed to come off like a true heroine. Now, I ask you, what do all heroines have in common? Bravery. I decided we should go with the scared-but-brave approach. I figured guys love that. Not that I actually *knew* any guys, but it always works in the movies. *(Re-enters scene. COURTNEY is now hooked up to an identical smiley-face IV.)*

JANICE. There! Now you and Star match! *(JANICE exits.)*

COURTNEY. I hate this thing. My hand hurts.

STAR. It's making you kind of pale. Pale is good. Remember, scared but brave. Now we need to improvise the script.

COURTNEY. What do you mean, improvise?

STAR *(to audience)*. It's *so* difficult to work with amateurs. *(Re-enters scene.)* It means make up the dialogue. Pretend I'm him and you're you.

COURTNEY. I feel like a total idiot!

STAR. Courtney, I'm doing this for you. Who is the experienced one here?

COURTNEY. Okay, okay. What do I do?

STAR. Pretend I'm Tom. I'm walking into the room.

(STAR walks to the door. A FLUNKY sprays her throat as she takes a very theatrical "moment" then crosses the room. She has become "TOM." She poses like a bad Shakespearean actor, speaks in a deep and stilted voice.)

STAR *(as "Tom")*. Hello, Courtney. How delightful to see you.

COURTNEY. How delightful to see you? If Tom was lame enough to say "How delightful to see you" would I be going out with him?

STAR *(as herself)*. Okay, my first drafts are sometimes a little stilted. We'll start again. *(To audience.)* Let's face it, I had absolutely no idea how a popular, cool thirteen year-old guy talks to a popular, cool thirteen year-old girl. And then it came to me. I could make him sound like a younger version of the incredibly cool and popular guy from *Hot House Princess*, Tony! *(Re-entering scene, she swaggers into the room, mimes wiping her nose, scratching her arm-*

pit, and adjusting her crotch. Speaks in a guy's voice with a heavy New York accent.) Yo, babe, how youse doin'?

COURTNEY *(stiffly).* Oh, hi, Tom. I am fine. How are you?

STAR *(to audience).* As you can see, she wasn't a born actress. I pressed on. *(Re-entering scene with the guy's voice.)* So, babe, what's the deal? Youse got the flu, or what?

COURTNEY *(disgusted).* Star, Tom doesn't have a New York accent.

STAR *(in her own voice).* Listen, Courtney, the first rule of improvisation is you never break character. Meaning that I am Tom, so don't call me Star. *(As "Tom.")* So babe, what can I do to make youse feel better? *(COURTNEY looks stumped. STAR stage whispers COURTNEY's line, in her own voice.)* Oh, nothing, I'll be fine.

COURTNEY *(deadpan).* Oh, nothing. I'll be fine.

STAR *(as "Tom").* You know, babe, I've tried. God knows I've tried. But it ain't the same without youse. Without youse, I don't got any dreams.

COURTNEY. Hey, that's what Tony says to Gloria in *Hot House Princess*!

STAR *(as herself).* I know that. I helped write it! *(She turns and shrugs to the audience, then re-enters scene as "Tom.")* You're so brave, babe.

COURTNEY. I have to be brave. For…for my father! He'll worry.

STAR *(as "Tom").* So, babe, will youse be better in time for the dance?

COURTNEY. Oh, yes!

STAR *(as "Tom").* If not, babe, hey, I'll understand. And I'll think about youse all night.

COURTNEY. What would you do, dance with that pig, Betsy Larski?

STAR (as "Tom"). No, I'd prob'ly dance widda 'nodda pig—

COURTNEY. You probably would. I know she likes you. You'll probably go to the dance with her. Your mother will probably make you! And all because I'm stuck in this stupid place with this stupid thing in my arm!

STAR (as herself, to audience). This was not going at all well. (Re-enters scene.)

COURTNEY. It's no use, Star! I can't do this! Either I can't say anything at all, or else I say something totally dweeby!

STAR. Maybe if I wrote out the lines for you—

COURTNEY. It's no use. It would be so much easier if Tom was here as a patient, like Jeff. If he could just get a *little* sick for a *little* while, we could both get better and go to the dance. (Beat.) Hey, I just thought of something!

STAR. What?

COURTNEY. You could invite Jeff in here, or we could go to Jeff's room! It would be so cool, two girls and two guys. I wouldn't have to try and figure out what to say every minute! It's perfect!

STAR. Oh, no, we couldn't, Jeff's pretty sick—

COURTNEY. You visit him, so he must be able to have visitors. Oh, please say yes, Star. Please, please, please!

STAR (to audience). What could I do? I said yes. (Re-enters scene.)

COURTNEY (hugging STAR). Oh, thank you! There's no one else in the whole world like you!

STAR. Glad you think so. Well, I'll just, um, go clear things with my boyfriend...Jeff. (The lights fade on the room as STAR drags her IV across the stage, humming something like the Beatles' "She Loves You," stopping outside a door that says 2-B. To the audience). Okay, now you're saying to yourself: "not only is this girl a total liar, she is also totally screwed." Clearly, there was only one thing I could do. I had to go into that room and convince the guy in there to pretend to be my boyfriend. No problem.

(STAR knocks on the door. A light comes up on the other side of the door in Jeff's room. It is a comfortable-looking boy's room with twin beds. On a desk we see a Bible with a Star of David on the cover. We see JEFF LEVINE, sitting on the bed reading Tennis *magazine. He wears faded, ripped jeans and a blue tennis shirt.)*

JEFF *(calling through the door)*. Come in.

(STAR enters, dragging her IV.)

STAR. Hi.

JEFF. Hi.

STAR *(to audience)*. OH MY GOD HE'S SO CUTE! *(Re-enters scene.)* I thought I'd stop by and introduce myself, since you never come out of your room. I mean, it's fine if you don't come out of your room. I like to be alone myself.

JEFF. Then why are you here?

STAR. Well, I don't like to be alone *all* the time. My name's Star.

JEFF. Jeff. *(An awkward silence.)*

STAR. So, Jeff...what are you in for?

JEFF. What are *you* in for?

STAR. Cystic fibrosis. It's this lung thing. No problem.

JEFF. It's not a "lung thing."

STAR. You've got it, too??

JEFF. Nope.

STAR. Then how—?

JEFF *(terse)*. My sister, okay?

STAR *(wheels her IV to a chair and sits)*. You still didn't say why you're here.

JEFF *(mumbling)*. Because I can't sleep.

STAR. You what?

JEFF. I can't sleep.

STAR. You can't *sleep*?

JEFF *(disgusted, miming in fake ASL sign-language as he talks)*. I can't sleep and you can't hear.

STAR. No need to get so touchy. I just never heard of anyone who couldn't sleep.

JEFF. Well, now you have.

STAR. So is that why you don't come out of your room, because you're always in here trying to sleep?

JEFF. Something like that.

STAR. Can't you just try to sleep at home?

JEFF. Listen, no offense, but you ask too many questions.

STAR. Maybe you just don't give enough answers.

JEFF *(standing)*. Hey, I didn't invite you in here!

STAR *(standing)*. Yes you did! I knocked and you said "come in"!! *(They scowl at each other. STAR stares up at him. He stares back. It is a stare-down. Neither blinks. Then finally.)* You have a hair sticking out of your left nostril.

JEFF. You have spinach in your teeth. *(A beat, then both turn away and quickly try to fix themselves: JEFF sticks his pinky in his nose to move the hair up, STAR rubs furiously at her teeth. Then they realize they've been fooled, turn back to each other, and finally laugh. STAR's laugh turns into a cough. She can't stop. JEFF rubs her back in a circular motion until the coughing subsides.)* Better?

STAR *(taking a deep breath, willing herself not to cough)*. I'm fine.

JEFF. Maybe you'd better go lie down.

STAR. No, no, I'm really okay. *(She takes a big gulp of air and doesn't cough.)* See? *(She grins.)*

JEFF. I see. You have a great smile.

STAR *(smiling even brighter)*. I do?

JEFF. Yeah.

STAR. Thanks. *(To audience.)* Clearly this guy had great taste. Now was the time to ask him. Wish me luck.

(FLUNKIES and ALL TEENS pop out of hiding places, cheering STAR on enthusiastically.)

FLUNKIE #1. Good luck, Star!

FLUNKIE #2. We're rootin' for ya, babe!

FLUNKIE #1. Go for it! *(FLUNKIES and TEENS instantly disappear.)*

STAR *(re-enters scene)*. So, Jeff, the thing is, I have a favor to ask you.

JEFF. Yeah?

STAR. Well, could you...I mean would you...would you pretend to be my boyfriend for about an hour this evening?

JEFF. Would I *what*??

STAR *(backing towards the door, dragging her IV)*. Forget it! Forget I said anything! It was a joke! Yeah, that's what it was, I was only joking!

JEFF. You want me to pretend to be your boyfriend?

STAR. Did I say that?

JEFF. That's what I heard. Why would you want me to pretend to be your boyfriend?

STAR. Oh, just this guy is coming over to see my roommate, and I *might* have said my boyfriend was in this room. And my roommate *might* have said it would be cool for her and this guy to hang out with me and my boyfriend. But look, just forget the whole thing. It was a stupid idea.

JEFF. I'll do it.

STAR *(not hearing him)*. So, I'm leaving. I'm gone. I'm outta here. It's been real—*(STAR fumbles to get the door open.)*

JEFF. Hey, I said I would do it.

STAR. You'll do it? But why?

JEFF. Because you're cute.

STAR. I am?

JEFF. So how long have we been together?

STAR. I'm cute?

JEFF. You *must* know you're cute.

STAR. Oh, sure. Guys tell me I'm cute all the time. The cutest. Hey, do you actually have a girlfriend? I mean, I don't care, I'm just curious.

JEFF. Not at the moment.

SALLY *(calling in from other side of the door)*. Star, are you in there?

STAR *(with a sigh, calling back)*. Yeah.

(SALLY enters. She has put on an over-done pretty shirt, and too much makeup.)

SALLY *(crossing to JEFF)*. Hi, I'm Sally.

JEFF. Jeff. *(To STAR.)* Is this your roommate?

SALLY. Oh no, I'm not Star's roommate. My roommate is an absolute child. I hope Star isn't disturbing you.

JEFF. Nope.

SALLY. Because she can be very dramatic at times. She thinks she's a professional *lesbian*.

STAR. You mean *thespian*. *An actor is a thespian!*

SALLY. I knew that. *(To JEFF.)* So, tell me all about yourself.

STAR *(dragging SALLY out)*. We're leaving, Sally.

SALLY. But I just got here! It's not fair! Why do I get left out of everything?

STAR *(to JEFF)*. I'll be back later. If you're sure it's okay...

JEFF. It's okay. See ya. *(As the lights fade on Jeff's room, STAR and SALLY exit into the hall and walk during their conversation.)*

SALLY. Why are you going back later?

STAR. None of your business.

SALLY. Can I come, too?

STAR. No.

SALLY. Why not?

STAR. Because.

SALLY. Because why?

STAR. Because you're not invited, okay?

SALLY. That's the thanks I get for doing your spying for you. I won't forget this, Star! *(SALLY flounces off.)*

STAR *(to audience)*. Frankly, I was too elated to worry about Sally. Jeff Levine liked my smile. He said I was cute. He said he'd pretend to be my boyfriend.

(Lights up on Star and Courtney's room as STAR enters. It is that evening. COURTNEY is dressed in a cute preppy-type outfit. She is still hooked up to the IV, and sings something like "She Loves You" as she looks in a mirror.)

COURTNEY. How do I look?

STAR. Cuter than Alicia Silverstone.

COURTNEY. Thanks. Aren't you going to change?

STAR. This is okay.

COURTNEY. It needs...something. *(She studies STAR.)* I know just the thing! *(COURTNEY rummages in her suitcase and pulls out a bangle bracelet.)* Try it. *(COURTNEY helps STAR put on the bracelet.)* Sexy! Oh, and one more thing. *(COURTNEY takes a long chain necklace with a*

*large heart on the end of it from around her neck and
gives it to STAR to put on.)*

STAR. I love it!

COURTNEY. It looks great on you! I got it at the coolest
shop, near Vanderbilt. We'll have to go there together
when we get out of here. They've got the greatest stuff.

STAR *(trying to sound casual).* Cool.

COURTNEY. We can go to the Bellevue mall, too. I saw the
cutest bathing suit at Dillard's. It's hot pink. I don't know
if it covers enough in the back, though. You know how
gross that is. Anyway, you'll tell me if I look like a cow in
it, won't you?

STAR. Absolutely. There's nothing worse than a girl who's
trying too hard.

COURTNEY. I want to get a John Lennon t-shirt, too, just
like yours! We're going to have an absolute blast!
(COURTNEY turns to the mirror.)

STAR *(turns to audience).* Maybe it *could* really happen. It
wasn't impossible. I refused to think about how I could
faint, or not be able to breathe, or—this is so gross—cough
up blood right there in the mall. The thing is, I had never
had a friend to go shopping with. I always went with Claudia. I'd see girls shopping together at the mall, running
around, flirting with guys…and it was like I was looking
through glass. If I could smash it I would, and then I'd
walk right through, and I'd be one of them. *(Re-enters
scene.)*

COURTNEY. You'd better tell me what's wrong with Jeff. I
don't want to say anything mega-embarrassing while we're
in his room.

STAR. It's this very rare sleeping sickness.

COURTNEY. Wow. How did he get it?

STAR. Mountain climbing with his father. In Peru.

(During the conversation we have been hearing THE TORTURER's theme music, but STAR is too involved to notice. Now THE TORTURER stands in the doorway.)

THE TORTURER *(ominously)*. Good evening. It's time.

STAR *(to audience)*. Evening thumps! I had managed to block it from my mind. What if she was in the middle of it and Tom showed up? It would be totally humiliating. And I'd be all sweaty and disgusting looking when I went to Jeff's room. No way. *(Re-enters scene. Scared to death, trying not to show it.)* Gee, sorry. I should have called to cancel. I'm not doing thumps tonight.

THE TORTURER *(looming)*. Of course you are.

STAR. No, I'm not.

THE TORTURER. I have no time for your nonsense. Now assume the position!

STAR. No. And you can't make me.

THE TORTURER *(threatening)*. Stella Grubner...

STAR. Star! My name is Star! And I'm not doing it tonight! *You* don't control me! *I* control me! *(THE TORTURER and STAR have a Wild West-style stare-down, complete with fake pistols, done to something like the theme music from "The Good, the Bad, and the Ugly." THE TORTURER looks like she wants to kill STAR, but STAR won't back down. Finally, THE TORTURER is beaten, she turns and exits, whimpering, mortified in defeat.)*

COURTNEY. You were fantastic!

STAR. I can't believe I did it! I stood up to The Torturer! And I won!

(TOM LOWELL knocks on the door. He is cute but slightly dweeby in an endearing way, forced by a parent to wear

*dress clothes for his visit and practically catatonic with
fear. He carries a bouquet of flowers.)*

STAR. Come in.

TOM *(entering the room)*. Hi. *(TOM thrusts the flowers at
COURTNEY, way too close to her face.)*

COURTNEY *(flustered, taking the flowers)*. Oh, thanks. I'll
find some water. I mean, I know where there's water. I
meant I didn't know where to put the water. What to put
the water in—

STAR. I'll do it. I'm Courtney's roommate, Star.

TOM. Tom. *(STAR crosses to the bathroom for water for the
flowers. TOM sits.)*

COURTNEY. Have a seat. Oh, I guess you already did.
*(COURTNEY sits. She and TOM stare at each other and
smile, unable to speak. STAR returns, the flowers in a
glass.)*

TOM. So I heard you were kinda sick.

COURTNEY. Just a little. *(Indicating her IV.)* Don't mind
this thing.

TOM *(taking forever to reply)*. Okay.

COURTNEY. So how's school?

TOM *(taking even longer)*. Okay.

COURTNEY. How's...the football team doing?

TOM *(even longer)*. Okay. *(COURTNEY gives STAR a desperate look.)*

STAR. Hey, I've got a great idea. My boyfriend is just down
the hall. Why don't we go down to his room?

COURTNEY. Great idea! Isn't that a great idea?

TOM *(barely able to find the right word)*. ...Okay.

COURTNEY *(as all three cross to the door)*. How's uh, geometry? *(An excruciating silence yet again as TOM tries to
form words.)*

STAR *(finally, to audience)*. Who wants to bet me it was "okay?" *(The light fades on the room as STAR, COURTNEY and TOM cross into the hall. To audience.)* I was a total wreck walking down to Jeff's room. What if he changed his mind? What if he had forgotten all about me? Or even worse, what if he had finally fallen asleep? *(Re-enters scene.)*

(The lights come up on JEFF in his room. STAR, COURT-NEY and TOM stand outside his door. STAR knocks.)

JEFF *(calling)*. Come in.

(STAR, COURTNEY and TOM enter.)

STAR. Hi, Jeff. This is my roommate, Courtney, and this is Tom. And this is my boyfriend, Jeff.

TOM *(totally comfortable now that he's talking about sports)*. Hey, I recognize you! You play tennis at the University School, right?

JEFF *(uncomfortable)*. Yeah.

TOM. My older brother played you a few weeks ago. Andy Lowell from Donelson? I saw that match. Man, you were awesome! You beat him in straight sets, and my brother is the best guy on the varsity. That put you in the all-state semifinals, right?

JEFF *(clearly uncomfortable)*. Yeah.

TOM *(eagerly)*. So how were the semis?

JEFF *(obviously wanting to change the subject)*. Hey, how's my girlfriend today?

TOM. But—

JEFF *(ignoring TOM, to STAR)*. You're looking hot. But then, you always do.

COURTNEY. Have you and Star been together a long time?

JEFF / STAR *(simultaneously)*. No / Yes.

STAR. I mean, that depends on what you call a long time.

JEFF. Right. The long time has gone by so fast that it seems like a short time.

COURTNEY *(knowingly)*. I heard about your younger brother.

JEFF. My younger bro—?

STAR *(interrupting)*. You know. Your brother. *Ken.* The one who introduced us *that fateful day.*

JEFF. Ah, yes. That fateful day.

COURTNEY. Is he still speaking to you, after what happened?

JEFF / STAR *(simultaneously)*. Yes / No.

STAR. What he means is Ken doesn't talk about that fateful day, but he still talks.

JEFF. Yeah, he talks!

TOM. Wait until I tell Andy I met you. He told me you were the best player he's ever played.

JEFF. Hey, it's only a game. It's not important.

TOM. Are you kidding? Andy says—

(SALLY and JANICE appear outside the door. JANICE is carrying her guitar. SALLY breezes in. She has changed into an awful, colorful outfit. JANICE follows.)

SALLY. Hey, kids!

STAR *(with a big, fake grin)*. Why, Sally, what a surprise. What are you doing here?

SALLY. Oh, I overheard y'all saying there was a party in here tonight. Hi Jeff, remember me?

JANICE *(sitting on the other bed, strumming the guitar)*. Everybody know this one? *(JANICE begins to play and sing something like* "Kum Ba Yah.") I'll go over the words. It goes: Kum Ba Yah, my Lord. Kum Ba Yah.

JEFF. What does that mean?

COURTNEY. Star asked the same thing! That is so romantic! I think it's so cute when couples think exactly alike.

SALLY. What are you talking about? They're not a couple. They just met.

STAR. We did not! He's my boyfriend!

SALLY. Star, you are such a big, fat liar!

JANICE. Maybe we should try a different song...

COURTNEY. Star is not a liar!

SALLY. She is so! Star doesn't have a boyfriend!

STAR. I do too!

TOM. I think Jeff's brother introduced them or something—

SALLY. Oh, sure. Star asked me to spy on him just this morning, so she could find out about him. Isn't that true, Star?

JANICE. Who knows "Puff the Magic Dragon"? It goes: *(She starts playing and singing, but she peters out since no one is paying attention).*

SALLY *(taunting STAR).* Why don't you just tell everyone the truth for once?

COURTNEY. Please tell Sally the truth so she'll shut up. *(Everyone stares silently at STAR.)*

STAR. I...I...I...*(STAR is stuck in excruciating limbo for two long beats. Then JEFF gets up, crosses to STAR, and kisses her.)*

COURTNEY *(to SALLY).* Well! I guess that shows you!

STAR *(to audience, beyond ecstatic).* Whoa, baby! Yes! Just in case any of you were in the bathroom and just now got back to your seat, I offer you...The Instant Replay. *(STAR and JEFF back up into the scene.)*

SALLY *(taunting STAR)*. Why don't you just tell everyone the truth for once?

COURTNEY. Please tell Sally the truth so she'll shut up.

STAR. I...I...I...*(Everyone resumes exact positions of the first kiss. JEFF gets up, crosses to STAR, and kisses her more fully. STAR moves downstage as the lights fade on the bedroom. To audience.)* I *love* that part! Anyway, right after that, Sally ran out screaming that everyone was against her, Janice left in search of perkier patients, Tom said his dad was waiting downstairs, and finally Courtney and I went back to our room. At least I think that's what happened. It's hard to remember, because I was busy re-living the absolutely most perfect moment of my life. When Jeff Levine kissed me.

(As STAR narrates the action, each character repeats their lines in a high voice, sotto voce, and runs out of the room like a manic cartoon character on fast-forward. Lights up on Star and Courtney's bedroom as STAR enters. During the following conversation they change for bed.)

COURTNEY *(drawing the curtain around her bed so that we see only STAR)*. Jeff is the coolest guy I ever met in my life.

STAR *(blissed out)*. Tom is nice, too.

COURTNEY. He seems so young next to Jeff. Star, remember when you told me you actually Did It with Jeff's younger brother, because you wanted to make Jeff jealous?...

STAR. Mmmm hmmmm......

COURTNEY. Was that true?

STAR. No. I can't lie to you. It wasn't true.

*[Note: Alternative lines for here are at end of Act Three.]

COURTNEY. I didn't think so.

STAR *(gleefully letting the audience in on this lie).* But I did *touch* it.

COURTNEY. Wow! You actually *touched* it??

STAR *(making it up as she goes along).* Yeah. By mistake. My hand kind of brushed against it.

COURTNEY. What did it feel like?

STAR. A great, big, huge…*(Trying to think of something, she looks at the IV pole.)* snake!!

[End alternative lines.]

COURTNEY *(in awe).* Wow…*(COURTNEY opens the curtains, both girls have finished changing. STAR wears an oversized t-shirt, COURTNEY wears a frilly flannel nightgown.)* One other thing. You know how in that scene you wrote the girl tried to kill herself? Well, you didn't really try to—

STAR. Never happened.

COURTNEY. Good.

STAR. No problem.

COURTNEY. Did you see the look on Sally's face when she ran out of the room?

STAR. It was priceless!

COURTNEY *(reaches over and turns out the light. The stage goes to black).* 'Night, Star. I had the greatest time tonight.

STAR. Me, too. *(STAR coughs, then clears her throat. She coughs again, longer and deeper.)*

COURTNEY. Star, are you okay?

STAR *(struggling).* Sure. Sorry if I'm keeping you awake. *(More coughing, gagging.)*

COURTNEY. Star? Star?

STAR. Courtney, I think I'm going to—*(STAR coughs and wretches deeply. COURTNEY snaps on the light. STAR is covered in blood. She can't stop coughing, gasping for air.)*

COURTNEY *(horrified)*. Oh, my God! *(Running to the door, screaming.)* Help! Somebody come help! Please! Somebody! *(COURTNEY stands at the door screaming and crying hysterically, STAR coughs and gasps for breath, the lights fade. Quickly, music up: something like the Beatles' "Hey Jude.")*

END OF ACT TWO

ACT THREE

AT RISE: *Music up: something like the theme from "Rocky."*
A spot picks up FLUNKIES and STAR, jogging single- file
through the audience. STAR wears a satin prizefighter's
robe with a huge star on the back, and boxing gloves, the
FLUNKIES wear their usual outfits and sunglasses. The
first FLUNKY keeps the audience away from STAR saying
"make way for the champ, get back," etc., as they head for
the stage. The second FLUNKY jogs behind the first, and
STAR's gloves rest on the second FLUNKY's shoulders.
Other FLUNKIES might run down the aisles of the theatre
with autograph books, screaming for STAR's autograph
like rabid fans. STAR might do short boxing choreography,
followed by push-ups, as the FLUNKIES count them off.
Then the FLUNKIES stand on either side of STAR, looking
mean, acting as her ring seconds and bodyguards.

STAR *(to audience).* What do you think of the robe? *(She
turns around to show the big star on the back.)* Pretty happening, huh? *(STAR holds out her hands and the FLUNK-
IES take off her boxing gloves in perfect syncopation, then
resume their positions.)* So, here we are, Act Three. When
last we saw The Champ—meaning me—things were not
looking too good. We pick up the story the next morning,
which is good news, since it means I didn't croak. The bad
news is I woke up in one of these. *(STAR holds her arms
out and the FLUNKIES take off her robe, turn, and jog off*

stage. STAR has on an ugly hospital gown.) Mondo-uggo. I could hear Dr. Scott and Claudia talking, but I was so out of it, it was like listening to them on the radio.

(The lights come up on DR. SCOTT and CLAUDIA in Star's room. She watches them argue about her.)

CLAUDIA. Look, I know all about the lung infection eroding a major artery. I understand that's why she hemorrhaged. But why did she bleed so much more this time?

DR. SCOTT. You know the answer to that.

CLAUDIA. She's been fine.

DR. SCOTT. Come on, Claudia. You know it's getting worse. Star knows it, too.

CLAUDIA. She's fine. She's a fighter.

DR. SCOTT. The second half's right.

CLAUDIA. When will she wake up?

DR. SCOTT. Hard to say when the tranquilizer will wear off.

CLAUDIA. At least it finally stopped her from coughing. She looked so...I just don't understand why Dr. Pemrose wasn't here. He's her doctor, for Crissake! You're just a resident!

DR. SCOTT *(chiding).* Come on, Claudia. I told you he's out of town—

CLAUDIA. —And he'll get here as soon as he can get here. I know, I know. I'm sorry, Scott. I'm just...damn, I need a cigarette.

DR. SCOTT. You want me to tell you everything will be okay and pat your hand in a comforting fashion?

CLAUDIA. I'd rather have the cigarette.

DR. SCOTT. Look, Claudia, you really do need to face what's going on here, you know...

CLAUDIA. Why? Give me one damn good reason why?

DR. SCOTT *(a beat)*. Call me if she wakes up. *(Exits.)*

STAR *(downstage, to audience)*. I did wake up, but I couldn't really talk for days and days. Imagine me, not talking! It was a fate *worse* than death! Claudia kept sneaking cigarettes, which is what finally put me over the edge. Excuse me. *(Simultaneous to STAR's speech, we see CLAUDIA. She paces the room, goes to her purse, pulls out a cigarette and places it between her lips. She lights a match. STAR holds her hospital gown closed and crosses into the scene, getting into bed, reattaching her IV. In a hoarse voice.)* Don't light that.

CLAUDIA. You're awake!

STAR *(speaking with difficulty)*. You bought cigarettes.

(DR. SCOTT enters the hallway. He stops outside STAR'S door, listening.)

CLAUDIA. I'm sick of getting fat from the candy. How do you feel?

STAR. Okay.

CLAUDIA. Of course you're okay. Nothing keeps my girl down, right?

STAR. Right. Where's Courtney?

CLAUDIA. I don't know. Do you remember what happened?

STAR *(it comes flooding back to her)*. Oh, God. I can't believe that happened in front of Courtney. She's going to hate me...

CLAUDIA. No one could hate you. I have to get Scott. He said to get him when you—

DR. SCOTT *(entering the room. Angry at CLAUDIA)*. I heard you talking. *(To STAR.)* Hi, there.

STAR. Hi.

DR. SCOTT. How do you feel?

STAR. Is everyone going to keep asking me that?

DR. SCOTT. You had a bit of a scare, huh?

STAR. I'm fine.

DR. SCOTT. It must have been scary, though. It's okay to say so.

STAR. I was so scared I was going to di—

CLAUDIA *(cutting her off)*. Don't tell her to be scared if she's not, for Chrissake!

STAR *(very guilty)*. Did this happen because I didn't do thumps?

CLAUDIA. You missed your thumps??

STAR. I skipped them the night I got sick. The Torturer came and I refused!

DR. SCOTT *(gently)*. Star, you can't refuse to do your therapy.

STAR. This is my fault!

DR. SCOTT. It might have happened anyway. Don't blame yourself, okay?

(JANICE enters holding a syringe. She crosses to STAR. She looks and speaks normally, no longer chirpy.)

JANICE. Hey, sweetie! Glad to see you're awake. I'm going to give you a shot of vitamin K. It'll help your blood clot more quickly. Just a little turn...(*JANICE gently turns STAR on her side and gives her the shot.)* There, now. All through. No more needles. *(JANICE strokes STAR's hair.)*

DR. SCOTT. Star, your mom and I are going down the hall for a little chat, then we'll be back, okay?

STAR. Sure. But try and say something more interesting than the junk you've been saying in here all week.

CLAUDIA. We didn't think you were awake. *(DR. SCOTT and CLAUDIA exit.)*

JANICE. How would you like it if I got my guitar and sang some songs just for you?

STAR. Oh gee, Janice, don't trouble yourself...

JANICE. Pooh, it's no trouble!

(COURTNEY appears at the doorway. She's dressed in jeans. Her IV is gone.)

COURTNEY. I heard she's awake.

JANICE. She is, isn't that great? I'll just run and get my guitar. It won't take but a second. *(JANICE exits.)*

COURTNEY *(crosses to STAR's bed)*. Hi.

STAR. Hi.

COURTNEY. How are you feeling?

STAR. Geez, I should just make a recording. I'm fine. What did I miss while the lights were out?

COURTNEY. Why are you making jokes?

STAR. Why not?

COURTNEY. Why not? That is a stupid thing to say! You scared me to death last week!

STAR. Hey, you needed a little excitement in your life. You must be better, they took your IV out.

COURTNEY. Listen, about last week. That was the worst thing I ever saw—

STAR. Don't make such a big deal out of it—

COURTNEY. But it was a big deal—

STAR *(putting her hands over her ears)*. You're boring me!

COURTNEY. Stop it! I have to talk to you—

(As COURTNEY delivers the next speech, STAR, her hands still over her ears, sings something like the opening lines of "She Loves You" as loud as she can to drown out COURTNEY.)

COURTNEY. It was so awful! I thought you were going to die! The blood was everywhere! All that blood—

STAR *(uncovering her ears)*. Big deal, what's a little blood between friends?

COURTNEY. Friends? We're not friends!

STAR *(a beat)*. Okay. We're not friends. *(A beat.)* Listen, I've been meaning to tell you. I'm going to be pretty busy, working on this new play I'm thinking about writing. So I don't think I'm going to have time to go shopping with you or anything. No offense.

COURTNEY. Why are you talking about shopping? Why are you acting like such an idiot?

STAR. You're the idiot!

COURTNEY. I'm not the one who almost died!

STAR. Just leave me alone.

COURTNEY. Why didn't you tell me?

STAR. Tell you what?

COURTNEY. Tell me how sick you are!

STAR. I'm not that sick!

COURTNEY. You're not? Then why have you lived practically all your life in Heart House? Sally told me the truth, which is more than I can say for you.

STAR. Sally should just—

COURTNEY *(interrupting)*. Why don't you go to school?

STAR. I told you why, because I'm an actress—

COURTNEY *(interrupting)*. That's not why. It's because of your cystic fibrosis.

STAR. All it means is that I cough sometimes—

COURTNEY *(angrily grabs a folded piece of paper from her back pocket. She unfolds it and reads it out loud)*. "Cystic fibrosis is a disease of every mucus-secreting gland. Excessive mucus production in the lungs ultimately leads to airway plugging and subsequent bacterial colonization and infection. This disease is fatal. The cause of death is chronic respiratory failure. In some patients bleeding from the lungs may result in death due to choking and shock."

STAR. I underestimated you. You *are* bright enough to use a dictionary.

COURTNEY. Why didn't you just tell me the truth?

STAR. I don't owe you anything.

COURTNEY. I guess not. But it's just that I thought you really cared about me. I thought we were best friends. But you didn't even care about me enough to tell me the truth.

STAR. But you hate sick kids!

COURTNEY. I never said that!

STAR. You did too! You said you were so glad your roommate wasn't really sick. You said the kids who had cancer were so gross because they lost their hair.

COURTNEY. I didn't mean it!

STAR. And Lee, the kid with AIDS. You and Julie wanted to wash your hands if you were even in the same *room* with him. What was I supposed to say? "Guess what, Courtney, I'm one of *them!*"

COURTNEY. I didn't understand—

STAR. Well, most people don't. Which is exactly why I don't tell anyone.

COURTNEY (*a beat*). So...I guess you don't want to be friends with me after all, then.

STAR. You're the one who said we weren't friends.

COURTNEY. Because I thought you lied to me for no good reason. But I was wrong.

STAR. No problem.

COURTNEY. So I guess you wouldn't want to hang out with me when I get out of here, after how stupid I was.

STAR. That depends on what level of stupid we're talking about. Are we talking Sally-type stupid, or are we talking there's hope-type stupid?

COURTNEY. There's hope. I hope.

STAR. Well then, I guess I could hang out with you.

COURTNEY. Great! We'll have a total blast. We'll go to the movies, we'll go to the mall. It just has to be on a day when you're feeling okay. Right?

STAR. Right.

COURTNEY. So then...*(Imitating STAR.)* no problem! *(The lights fade on the bedroom as STAR walks downstage.)*

STAR *(to audience).* So, go figure. Courtney knew the truth, and she wanted to be my friend anyway, even after she got out of the slammer. *(A beat.)* Well, can you blame her? *(STAR exits. From Star's tape deck we hear something like "Michelle" by the Beatles.)*

(Lights up on the bedroom. JULIE sings along to the music and dances with her boom-box. COURTNEY enters wearing a John Lennon t-shirt. She is sprawled on her bed. JULIE is sprawled on the floor. They are eating popcorn and laughing hysterically.)

COURTNEY. I can't believe your bathing suit got completely see-through once it got wet! I would have died! I would have absolutely died!

(STAR enters. She is dressed exactly as she was at the beginning of the play, minus the Jets baseball-style cap.)

STAR *(to audience).* It was a week later. They tried some new antibiotics on me, and they worked. I even got rid of that bogus IV. As for Courtney, Dr. Scott told her she'd probably be sprung within a day or two, so she was as happy as a tick on a bloodhound—they actually say that kind of stuff in Tennessee. *(STAR enters the scene, crossing into the bedroom, grabs some popcorn, sits on the floor. JULIE starts playing with Star's hair.)*

JULIE. I made Kurt turn around and promise not to look while I got out of the pool, and then he, like, whips around and stares at me with this big grin on his face, and he goes: "I had my fingers crossed!" *(All three girls shriek.)*

COURTNEY. That is so immature. Isn't it, Star?

STAR. Totally.

COURTNEY. Well, you have such a totally cool boyfriend, he'd never do anything that obnoxious. *(To JULIE.)* You should see Star's boyfriend. The coolest. He's *fifteen.*

JULIE *(very impressed)*. Fifteen?

COURTNEY. And he's so-o-o cute. He kissed Star right in front of me.

JULIE. Awesome. When a guy does that you know he really, really likes you. You are so lucky.

STAR. Luck has nothing to do with it.

COURTNEY. If I could only learn to act that way around Tom...

JULIE. Hey, Tom really likes you!

COURTNEY. How do you know?

JULIE. He was talking about you in school.

COURTNEY. No way!

JULIE. Way!

COURTNEY. Tell me everything he said, word for word.

JULIE. He was talking to a bunch of us at lunch yesterday. And he said how you were so brave about being sick, and he goes: "no lie, I really admire her attitude."

COURTNEY. Oh my gosh, it worked! It was all Star's idea!

STAR. True. *(STAR turns the volume up on her tape player. We hear the beginning of something like* "She Loves You.") Hey! Let's do my big number from *Hot House Princess!* *(STAR gets up and begins to do choreography from* Hot House Princess. *She pulls JULIE and COURTNEY up to join her. The three girls dance and sing along lustily with the chorus, pretending various objects in the room are microphones. STAR begins to cough. COURTNEY goes to her and pats her on the back. JULIE turns off the music.)*

COURTNEY. Better?

STAR. No problem.

JULIE *(looking at her watch)*. I gotta go. My mother the motor-mouth is downstairs. She's probably told everyone who's passed by the story of my life by now. When are y'all getting out of here?

COURTNEY. Soon, thank God.

JULIE. We should, like, give a party or something.

COURTNEY. Hey, I've got a great idea! I should give a party after the school dance next week. You know it'll end really early. And Star can come!

JULIE. Get real, Courtney. Your mom will never let you give a boy-girl party. She says prayers every night that you'll become allergic to, like, the entire boy half of the population!

COURTNEY. True. But these are extenuating circumstances, *(Dramatically, throwing her hand to her forehead.)* after I was so deathly ill and all. I'll work on my dad, and he'll convince my mom. I know he will! And it would be so cool if you come, Star.

JULIE. Could you? And bring Jeff? It would be totally awesome.

STAR. I'll have to check my datebook.

COURTNEY *(throwing a pillow at her)*. Get out of here!

STAR. Okay, you talked me into it.

JULIE *(hugging COURTNEY and STAR good-bye)*. Great! So I'll call y'all later and we'll plan it and everything. It's gonna be awesome! Like, really awesome. Like really, totally awesome! Love y'all! *(JULIE runs out.)*

COURTNEY. You'll be okay for the party, won't you?

STAR. Yeah. Dr. Scott will spring me for a few hours, unless I'm in really bad shape, which I won't be.

COURTNEY. Great! And no one has to know you're in Heart House—unless you want them to.

STAR. I won't.

COURTNEY. Hey, let's go invite Jeff!

STAR. Great idea! *(To audience.)* Uh-oh. I was in deep doo-doo. It was one thing for Jeff to pretend to be my boyfriend at Heart House, and quite another to expect him to do it out in the real world. *(Re-entering the scene.)* On second thought, I don't think he'd want to come.

COURTNEY. Sure he would!

STAR. Maybe he, uh, doesn't really like me all that much.

COURTNEY. Star, he kissed you right in front of everybody.

STAR. Well, yeah. But he hasn't even come around since I was sick. He can't be too busy. A person who doesn't sleep has a lot of free time on his hands.

COURTNEY. I *know* he really likes you. When you got sick I ran down to his room—I knew he'd want to know. He was really worried about you.

STAR. He was?

COURTNEY. He's the one who gave me all that stuff I read to you about cystic fibrosis. It's from a paper he wrote for school. *(The lights fade on the bedroom as STAR walks downstage.)*

STAR *(to audience).* Right then, something clicked in my head. Suddenly it all made sense. Jeff. And me. And his little sister who had cystic fibrosis.

(Lights up on Jeff's room. He is reading a book called, When Bad Things Happen to Good People. *STAR marches in, furious, without knocking.)*

STAR. You are a total jerk.

JEFF. Well, hi. Glad to see you're feeling better.

STAR. Yeah, like you care. Look, I don't need any more merciful gestures from you, okay?

JEFF. What are you talking about?

STAR. Oh sure, pretend you don't know. *(Mimicking JEFF.)* "You have a great smile. You're really cute." *(In her own voice.)* You must think I'm totally pathetic!

JEFF. No—

STAR. No? Where's your sister? The one who has cystic fibrosis?

JEFF. She doesn't have anything to do with this.

STAR. Yes she does. Where is she?

JEFF. She's dead. *(A beat.)* She died three months ago.

STAR. And that's why you wrote that paper on CF, because of her, right?

JEFF. I was trying to understand—

STAR. So you think I'm going to die, just like your sister, and that's why you pretended to like me. Because you felt *sorry* for me!

JEFF. You've got it wrong, I—

STAR. Well, I've got news for you. I'm not going to die! I'm just not. And I wouldn't have you for a boyfriend if you were the last guy on earth!

JEFF. Look, you're right. When you told me you had CF, it reminded me of my sister—

STAR. I knew it—

JEFF. —And I guess I agreed because of that. But only at first. Then I just liked you.

STAR. You are so full of it.

JEFF. Look, I *do* like you—

STAR. Oh sure, I guess that's why you've been hanging around my room, because you like me so much.

JEFF *(a beat)*. Sit down a minute.

STAR. I don't want to sit down.

JEFF. Please.

STAR *(sitting, sighing dramatically and rolling her eyes)*. Well?

JEFF. My little sister, Jessie, was the cutest kid. I was crazy about her. Only she was born with this horrible disease. I never really believed she'd die. But she did. She was eleven years old. It was right before I was supposed to play in the all-state semi-finals. You know how unimportant that seemed? Everyone was saying how great I was, and how brave I was, and it made me sick. I haven't played tennis since. And I haven't slept much, either.

STAR. You mean this sleeping thing is in your head, because of your sister?

JEFF. That's what the brilliant doctors say.

STAR. So am I supposed to feel sorry for you?

JEFF. Am I supposed to feel sorry for *you*?

STAR. No, you moron! That's the whole point!

JEFF *(catching a glimpse of his Bible on the desk)*. Do you believe in God?

STAR. What is this, a philosophy class?

JEFF. Do you?

STAR. Yeah, I guess.

JEFF. I don't. I want to, but I can't. If God can do anything, and God is good, then how could God let Jessie suffer and die?

STAR. Well, maybe God is good, but there's stuff He can't do.

JEFF. Then He isn't God.

STAR. Look, I don't have the answers. But I know I feel like there's something...bigger than me. That's all I know.

JEFF. Well, then, you know more than I do.

STAR. That's the first intelligent thing you've said since I came in here.

JEFF. You are a pain, you know that?

STAR. It's a gift.

JEFF (putting out his hand). Friends?

STAR. No. A friend would have come to my room to see how I was.

JEFF. I was scared. Because I like you. And I was afraid to like you too much...

STAR (finishing it for him). ...in case the same thing happened to me that happened to your sister. Well, all I have to say is, if you take the attitude that something bad might happen if you care about someone, then you'll never care about anyone.

JEFF. So would anything bad happen if I kissed you again?

STAR. I guess that's just a chance you'd have to take.

(The lights fade on Jeff's room as STAR walks downstage. As she speaks, a FLUNKY brings her a director's chair with a big star on the back, another FLUNKY hands her a megaphone.)

STAR (to audience). So he kissed me! We are talking *major* kiss here. This one I saved for posterity. You're gonna love it. (Sitting in the director's chair, speaking into the mega-

phone.) Okay, let's...roll 'em! *(On a large movie screen we see a dramatic close-up of JEFF and STAR dressed like Rhett Butler and Scarlett O'Hara. We hear something like the* Gone With the Wind *theme.)*

JEFF *(on the screen, à la Rhett).* So would anything bad happen if I kissed you again?

STAR *(on the screen, à la Scarlett).* I guess that's a chance you'd have to take. *(On the screen, JEFF kisses STAR à la a Hollywood movie. The music swells, "THE END" appears on the screen. The screen goes black. To audience.)* And a thunderous applause!

(FLUNKIES and TEENS run down the aisle screaming and applauding, then quickly exit.)

STAR *(continuing, to audience).* Tell me that isn't the most romantic thing you've ever seen in your life. And how about my close-up! I—

(SALLY comes stomping in.)

SALLY *(as she crosses).* Hold it, hold it, hold it, hold it! *(Standing next to STAR but in the dark, outside Star's light.)* Yo, you in the booth! Gimme a light! *(Nothing happens. She steps into Star's light.)* Thank you *so* much. *(To STAR.)* I really do not think this is fair. Why do you get all the kissing scenes? Why do you get to direct everything?

STAR. Because.

SALLY *(thinking a moment).* Oh. *(Exits.)*

(As the lights come up on Star and Courtney's bedroom, we see COURTNEY lying on her bed, making a list. As she speaks, STAR crosses and enters the scene.)

COURTNEY *(counting the names on her list)*. Jenny and Kyle, Kimber and Matt. Let's see…that makes twenty. You think twenty kids is too many?

STAR. Nah. Do we have the same number of guys and girls?

COURTNEY. Yeah, now that Jeff's coming. This'll be the first party I've ever given. I'm really nervous.

STAR. Hey, no problem! *(STAR coughs.)*

COURTNEY. You okay?

STAR. Yeah.

COURTNEY. I can't believe I'm finally going home tomorrow. I feel like I've been here *forever*.

STAR. Yeah, well, I actually *have*.

COURTNEY. It's going to be different now, though. We're going to do a zillion things together. You'll see. Oh, gosh, I forgot to put Sandra Carlton on the list! She'll kill me if I don't invite her.

(COURTNEY writes Sandra's name on her list. SALLY appears at the door.)

SALLY *(entering)*. Hey. What are y'all doing?

COURTNEY *(quickly shoves the party list under her pillow)*. Oh, nothing. Just hanging out.

SALLY *(to COURTNEY)*. I heard you're going home tomorrow.

COURTNEY. Yep.

SALLY. That's nice. My roommate left yesterday. She left me one of her Barbies, if you ever want to see it.

COURTNEY. Why would I want to see her Barbie?

SALLY *(trying to think of a reason)*. Maybe it's an antique. Hey, y'all want to go to the lounge and watch TV?

COURTNEY. No, thanks. We're busy now.

SALLY *(very sad)*. Oh, okay. Well, see ya. *(SALLY forlornly crosses to the door.)*

STAR. Hey, Sally, wait a sec. We're planning a party at Courtney's house next Saturday. Want to come?

SALLY *(face lights up)*. Are you serious?

STAR. Sure.

SALLY. Because if you're just saying it to make fun of me, it really, really is not fair. It's—

STAR. Get a grip, Sally. I'm serious.

SALLY *(it sinks in that she's really invited, then shyly)*. I'd love to come. *(SALLY exits walking on air.)*

COURTNEY. You're a saint.

STAR. Jews don't have saints, but I do like the sound of Saint Star.

(JANICE sticks her head in the door.)

JANICE. Hey, hey, girls! Just passing by. Courtney, I'll be right back to do your last EKG. *(JANICE exits.)*

COURTNEY. My last EKG! I love the sound of that!

STAR. You don't have to have them anymore?

COURTNEY. Well, yeah. I have to come back next week and have one. But this'll be my last one as a resident of the fabulous Heartless House. *(STAR starts coughing.)* That doesn't sound good.

STAR. I'm a little tired.

COURTNEY *(crossing to feel STAR's forehead)*. Do you have a fever? You're kind of flushed...

(CLAUDIA enters. She wears a great sexy outfit with a mini-skirt and carries an armload of school books.)

CLAUDIA *(dumping the books on the nightstand)*. Hey, girl-friend! These are compliments of Liza Jayne. Dr. Pemrose says you're well enough to start with your tutor again to-morrow.

STAR *(sarcastically)*. Gee, great news.

COURTNEY. Wow, nice outfit!

CLAUDIA. Thanks. I got it shipped from New York.

STAR *(to audience)*. She was wearing her good luck outfit. She only wore it when something really big happened. And then it dawned on me...*(Re-entering scene.)* Oh my God. It's that call you were waiting for. It's Broadway, right?

CLAUDIA. Not exactly.

STAR. Off-Broadway! So? That's still fabulous!

CLAUDIA. No. But I did get the lead in Franklin Community Theatre's next production. You are looking at Fanny Brice in *Funny Girl*!

COURTNEY *(hugging CLAUDIA)*. That is fantastic! We'll come to see it together, won't we, Star?

STAR *(trying to sound as if she means it)*. Sure. Absolutely.

CLAUDIA *(jumping up)*. Hey, want to go for a walk? I'm all antsy tonight.

STAR. Sure.

COURTNEY. But I thought you were ti—

STAR *(cutting her off)*. I'm fine. Want to come?

COURTNEY. Nah. I've got to do the geometry homework that Julie brought over. I just hate it. What does geometry have to do with anything in real life?

STAR. A question I've often asked myself.

COURTNEY *(getting her text and notebook out)*. If I can plow through this junk quick I'll come find you, okay?

STAR. Sure. And I'll be sure to tell your mommy how good you were, doing your homework first and everything.

COURTNEY *(laughing)*. Get out of here!

(As STAR and CLAUDIA exit, the lights fade on the bedroom and they walk towards the lounge. If possible Star's room should pivot so that we no longer see it. If this is not possible, we see NURSE JANICE enter with the EKG machine, then pull the curtain shut around Courtney's bed. After a few beats she runs out. After a few more beats she returns with THE TORTURER. They disappear behind the curtain. All this should be done unobtrusively, with as little light as possible. The action is simultaneous but our focus is on STAR and CLAUDIA in the lounge.)

CLAUDIA. You two have really gotten to be good friends, huh?

STAR. Best friends. Isn't she great?

CLAUDIA *(playfully)*. Hey, I thought *I* was your best friend.

STAR. She and I are going to have a total blast when she gets out.

CLAUDIA. Good, babe.

STAR. She really is going to be my friend, you know. Not just while she's in Heart House.

CLAUDIA *(apparent that she doesn't believe STAR)*. Great!

(The lights come up on the lounge. SALLY is in one corner by herself, reading her teen novel. STAR and CLAUDIA sit on the couch.)

STAR. So, are you psyched about this part?

CLAUDIA. Sure!

STAR. It doesn't matter about the big phone call from New York. Something else will come through.

CLAUDIA. That's show biz.

STAR. So what are you so bummed about?

CLAUDIA *(looking over at SALLY)*. That poor kid. She's so lonely. She doesn't really have any friends here, does she?

STAR. That's because she's obnoxious.

CLAUDIA. I'm so glad we're friends. That's how I think of you, you know, as my best friend.

STAR. Yeah, so if we're so close and everything why won't you tell me what's wrong?

CLAUDIA. You amaze me! Sometimes I think you're more grown up than I am!

STAR. I am. So...?

CLAUDIA. Oh, it's just...I guess I'm feeling—I don't know—old.

STAR. Because you didn't get the phone call from New York?

CLAUDIA. I shouldn't have counted on it so much. It's silly. I should be glad to get the lead in community theatre musicals. But you know, once I had all these dreams...

STAR. It could still happen.

CLAUDIA *(reaching in her purse for a cigarette)*. I'm not kidding myself anymore. There are girls arriving in New York every day who are younger than me, prettier than me, probably more talented than me. And let's face it, they're there, and I'm here. I'm not going to get any phone call.

(DR. SCOTT enters wearily and crosses to them.)

DR. SCOTT. Hi, there. How's it going?

CLAUDIA *(to DR. SCOTT)*. You look beat.

DR. SCOTT. I had to pull an all-nighter to cover at the hospital. So, Star, I hear you and Courtney are planning this blow-out party.

STAR. It's going to be awesome. And listen to this. I have a date with—

VOICE *(over intercom, loud, insistent).* Code blue. Code blue. Dr. Rhodes, second floor, stat.

DR. SCOTT. Excuse me—*(DR. SCOTT exits on the run. STAR, SALLY and CLAUDIA look fearful.)*

CLAUDIA. I wonder why they never call the room number when they call a code blue.

STAR. They don't want to scare all the other kids by letting them know who's about to kick the bucket.

VOICE *(over intercom).* Code blue, code blue, second floor, stat.

SALLY. It's Lee. I know it's Lee. And I wasn't even nice to him.

VOICE *(over intercom).* Code blue, code blue, second floor stat.

SALLY. I can't stand it. I have to go see if it's Lee.

STAR. I'll go with you. *(SALLY and STAR trade looks. They understand each other. The light fades on the lounge as STAR steps forward and addresses the audience.)* We ran to the guys' wing, down to Lee's room, expecting to see a huge commotion, but there wasn't one. So we headed for the girls' wing. And there at the end of the hall were nurses running in and out, loud voices, frantic activity. There was the code blue. It was my room.

(As STAR runs through the lounge and down the hall towards her room, DR. SCOTT simultaneously runs into Star's room, disappearing behind the curtain. A back light here will allow us to see the shadows of medical personnel and COURTNEY through the curtain. JEFF, LEE, ANNIE, SALLY, and CLAUDIA stand near the doorway.)

DR. SCOTT *(from behind the curtain).* What happened?

JANICE *(from behind the curtain).* She arrested.

STAR *(running into the doorway)*. What are they doing in my room?? Let me go! *(STAR tries to go in, JEFF stops her and holds her arms. STAR struggles.)*

JEFF. You can't go in. Something happened to Courtney.

STAR. That's crazy! That's nuts! She's going home tomorrow! *(SALLY reaches out to touch STAR's hand. STAR shakes her off.)*

DR. SCOTT *(inside the room)*. One, two, three...clear. Give me a reading!

JANICE. Blood pressure zero. Pulse zero. *(A high-pitched buzzer goes off.)*

DR. SCOTT. Come on, dammit! One, two, three...clear, give me numbers!

JANICE. Nothing.

(The high-pitched buzzer continues. Everyone knows what it means. There is silence in the room. CLAUDIA quietly enters the scene, watching STAR.)

STAR *(a wild cry)*. Nooooo! There's nothing wrong with her! *(LEE, ANNIE, JEFF and SALLY walk away silently. Death isn't a stranger to them. JANICE and THE TORTURER lift a sheet over COURTNEY's face. DR. SCOTT crosses to STAR who starts hitting him.)* What did you do? I want to see her.

DR. SCOTT. I'm so sorry, Star. Courtney's heart was damaged and it ruptured. There was nothing we could have done.

STAR. But that can't be true! Please, make it not be true.

DR. SCOTT. I'm so sorry.

(CLAUDIA comes up behind STAR. The lights fade on the hall. JANICE opens the curtains that surround COURTNEY's bed.)

CLAUDIA *(quietly).* Come on, baby, come on out of here.

STAR. No! She can't breathe! Take the sheet off her face!

CLAUDIA. It's okay, baby. It's going to be okay.

STAR *(crying, out of control).* No, it's not! Nothing is okay! Don't you understand? She was my friend! My very first friend!

CLAUDIA *(reaching for her).* It's okay, baby. I'll be your friend.

STAR. No! I don't want you to be my friend! I want you to be my mother!

CLAUDIA. I am, Star—

STAR. No! You *never* wanted to be my mother! You're Claudia, and I ruined your life. I want Courtney! I want my friend! *(DR. SCOTT carries COURTNEY out.)* Don't touch her!! Don't you touch her!! Don't hurt her…

THE TORTURER *(gently).* We won't hurt her, Star. *(JANICE and THE TORTURER follow DR. SCOTT.)*

CLAUDIA *(in a whisper).* I'm so sorry…

STAR. No—

CLAUDIA. Yes. It's okay not to be strong now, honey. It's okay to let go.

STAR. No—

CLAUDIA *(firmly).* Yes. It's okay. *(CLAUDIA holds out her arms to STAR. STAR hesitates.)* I'll be your mother, Star. I'll always take care of you. I'll never leave you. *(Finally, STAR runs into her arms.)*

STAR *(sobbing).* I'm so afraid I'll die. I don't want to die! I don't want them to cover my face with a sheet like they did to Courtney.

CLAUDIA *(rocking STAR in her arms).* Shhhhhh, it's okay, it's okay to cry…*(CLAUDIA continues to croon to STAR. She rocks STAR in her arms, as the lights fade. Blackout, CLAUDIA exits quickly. STAR steps forward into a light.)*

STAR *(to audience).* What a tear-jerker, huh? Just a sec...
*(Takes out a tissue and blows her nose noisily, then she
takes a couple of small packets of tissues out of her back
pocket.)* Anybody else need one? *(She throws the packs out
to two different people in the audience.)* So, anyway,
Courtney's funeral was two weeks ago. There were hun-
dreds of people there. I sat in the back with Lee, Sally, and
the other kids from Heart House. Everyone else sat apart
from us. And I guess they really *were* apart from us in a
certain way, and they always would be. I got sprung ten
days ago. Jeff came over once. I really like him. But what's
even more amazing is that Julie and her friend, Amy, came
over twice. We even went to the mall one day. Even if I do
live on the other side of the candy store window, sometimes it's fun to pretend I can go inside. There were a lot
of great things about Courtney, but the greatest of all was
that she accepted me completely, just as I am. And something about her accepting me made me start to accept me
too. It's just about the greatest gift anyone ever gave me.
And I believe she knows, and she's smiling down on me
right now, telling me that just like John Lennon, I should
enjoy every moment of my time on this planet, however
long it is. *(She pulls the heart-shaped locket COURTNEY
gave her out from under her shirt and holds the heart in
her hand.)* Thanks, Courtney. No problem. *(STAR smiles at
the audience and turns, walking slowly upstage. She pulls
her baseball cap out from some hiding place and sets it
backwards on her head, staring out at the audience. We
hear the simple melody of the final line of the same song
which has been our theme throughout, something like* "She
Loves You," *played plaintively on a flute, as the light fades.)*

CURTAIN—END OF PLAY

(see following page)

NOTE: The curtain call should be done to something like "She Loves You" by the Beatles, played really loud. The entire cast might be dressed in identical John Lennon t-shirts.

*(Alternative lines for mini-scene—begin at the asterisk on page 51.)

COURTNEY. I didn't think so. I wonder what it's like to...you know.

STAR. What?

COURTNEY (significantly). You know!

STAR. I think it must be totally wonderful, beautiful, and incredible.

COURTNEY. Wow.

STAR. On the other hand, it might be totally slimy, gross, and disgusting.

NOTES TO THE DIRECTOR

1) JOHN LENNON & ME has played successfully in this version to family audiences all over North America. However, should you prefer more conservative language in some places, the playwright makes the following suggestions:

    a. Star's anatomical reference on page 15 could be to "boobs" or something similar.

    b. Star's totally-concocted story on page 23 and Courtney's reference on page 51, could easily be changed to being about "Making Out."

    c. There's an asterisk at the beginning of the penultimate moment of Act Two, page 51, and following the final page of the play, an alternative series of lines is suggested.

    d. The photo of Patrick Swayze and all references to Patrick Swayze can be changed to the hot, young male movie star of the moment, if desired.

2) This story unfolds through the eyes of STAR. She often addresses the audience directly—as if to her <u>best friend and confidante</u>. THE FLUNKIES wear black pants and black t-shirts with a star and the words "STAR'S FLUNKY" inscribed on the front or back. They are as hip as the hippest rappers on MTV. FLUNKIES do all scene and set changes, all their movements should be choreographed as part of the play. The set might look very cartoony in Act One and Two, to emphasize the over-the-top version of the story we are seeing through STAR's eyes. In Act Two as STAR gets closer to reality, certain of these cartoon elements could be eliminated, and in Act Three, when STAR faces reality, we should see a totally realistic set. Likewise the look and acting style of the cast should be much broader early in the play and become more realistic as the play progresses. Old Beatles tunes might be used for pre-set, intermissions and wherever music is needed.

3) Approximate running time: About 90 minutes.
  Act One—32 minutes
  Act Two—29 minutes
  Act Three—33 minutes

A <u>pause</u> of five minutes is suggested between Act One and Act Two, an <u>intermission</u> of ten minutes suggested between Act Two and Act Three.

4) All music indicated in the script is suggested, and producers are reminded to clear rights as appropriate for any music actually used in individual productions.

CHARACTER NOTES

› STAR: Small for her age, thin, funny, feisty, irreverent, smart. She is unconventionally pretty and does everything with style, energy and confidence.
› COURTNEY CAMBRIDGE: Pretty cheerleader, starting to get a figure. Long blonde hair. She is sincere, naive, very popular, just getting over rheumatic fever.
› SALLY KASEM: Insecure, whiny, desperate to be liked, tries too hard.
› JULIE ROWEN: Pretty cheerleader or gymnast, baton twirler. Hyper, bubbly.
› TOM LOWELL: Shorter than Courtney, cute, shy around girls almost to the point of paralysis.
› JEFF LEVINE: Gorgeous, athletic, sensitive, deeply troubled.
› CLAUDIA GRUBNER: A rock 'n roller, very hip, an actress/singer/dancer.
› INA TORTUNESKY: Huge, formidable-looking, scary, every child's nightmare, deep-voiced.
› DR. SCOTT RHODES: Gorgeous, great build, kind, deeply caring.
› NURSE JANICE BOBRIN: Unbelievably perky, caring, a high chirpy voice, plays the guitar bacly.
› FLUNKY #1 & FLUNKY #2: Physical opposites, they do Star's bidding throughout the show, comic, very hip, athletic gymnasts and dancers.